PEARSON

LANGUAGE
CENTRAL

grade
1

ELD
Practice Book

PEARSON

Glenview, Illinois • Boston, Massachusettes • Chandler, Arizona • Upper Saddle River, New Jersey

Copyright © Pearson Education, Inc., or its affiliates.
All Rights Reserved. Printed in the United States of America. This publication is protected by copyright, and permission should be obtained from the publisher prior to any prohibited reproduction, storage in a retrieval system, or transmission in any form or by any means, electronic, mechanical, photocopying, recording, or likewise. For information regarding permissions, write to Pearson Curriculum Group Rights & Permissions, One Lake Street, Upper Saddle River, New Jersey 07458.

Pearson is a trademark, in the U.S. and/or other countries, of Pearson Education, Inc., or its affiliates.

ISBN-13: 978-0-328-63481-1
ISBN-10:   0-328-63481-6

PEARSON

1 2 3 4 5 6 7 8 9 10   V031   14 13 12 11 10

ISBN-13: 978-0-328-63481-1
ISBN-10:   0-328-63481-6

EAN

90000>

9 780328 634811

Copyright © Pearson Education, Inc., or its affiliates. All Rights Reserved.

Unit R Homes and Families

Unit 1 Animals, Tame and Wild

Unit 2 People in Communities

Copyright © Pearson Education, Inc., or its affiliates. All Rights Reserved.

Unit 3 Growing and Changing

Unit 4 Surprising Treasures

Unit 5 Clever Solutions

Copyright © Pearson Education, Inc., or its affiliates. All Rights Reserved.

Around Home

Vocabulary

bedroom	home	moved
green	favorite	see

Directions Match each word to its definition and picture.

1. bedroom _____ a room with a bed where you sleep

2. green   the place where you live

3. home   having the color of grass

4. moved   went to a new place to live

Directions Finish the sentences. Use words from the box.

5. I keep my toys in my **bedroom**.

6. I **see** a cat.

7. My **favorite** toy is a car.

Copyright © Pearson Education, Inc., or its affiliates. All Rights Reserved.

Name _____

The Sound /m/

Directions Look at each picture. Say the word. Write the word.

1. __m__ __a__ __n__

2. __m__ __o__ __p__

3. __d__ __r__ __u__ __m__

The Sound /s/ Spelled *s*

Directions Look at the picture. Say the word. Write the word.

4.  __s__ __a__ __w__

5. __s__ __u__ __n__

6.  __s__ __o__ __c__ __k__

Copyright © Pearson Education, Inc., or its affiliates. All Rights Reserved.

Describing

Directions Circle the word that describes the child in each picture.

1.    sad   (happy)

2.   (sick)   mad

Character

Directions Circle the characters in this picture.

Copyright © Pearson Education, Inc., or its affiliates. All Rights Reserved.

Name _____

People and Things

Directions Circle the pictures and words that show more than one thing or person.

 dogs

cat

book

balls

Directions Add a letter to make the nouns more than one.

1. girl __s__

2. book __s__

3. cat __s__

4. boy __s__

Directions Write the name of a thing in your classroom. Write the name of a person in your classroom.

5. Answers will vary. _____

6. Answers will vary. _____

Copyright © Pearson Education, Inc., or its affiliates. All Rights Reserved.

Produce Language

My Weekly Concept Journal

Directions Write your answers in the space provided.

Day 1 <u>Answers will vary.</u>

Day 2

Day 3

Day 4

Copyright © Pearson Education, Inc., or its affiliates. All Rights Reserved.

Name _____

Produce Language

My Weekly Concept Journal

Directions Answer the weekly question.

What is around us at home?

Answers will vary but should show

understanding of the Concept Goals:

• understand what a home is

• provide examples of things found

  in homes

• describe what people do in a home

Copyright © Pearson Education, Inc., or its affiliates. All Rights Reserved.

Our Family

Vocabulary

baby	grandpa	like
grandma	care	together

Directions Match each word to its definition and picture.

1. baby

   to feel interest in or concern about someone or something

2. grandma

   your grandmother

3. grandpa

   a very young child

4. care

   your grandfather

Directions Finish the sentences. Use words from the box.

5. My family eats dinner __**together**__.

6. The __**baby**__ sleeps in a crib.

7. I __**like**__ my family.

Copyright © Pearson Education, Inc., or its affiliates. All Rights Reserved.

Name _____

The Sound /k/ Spelled *c*

Directions Look at each picture. Say the word. Write the word.

1. c a n

2. c a t

3.  c a r

The Sound /p/ Spelled *p*

Directions Look at the picture. Say the word. Write the word.

4.  p i g

5.  p a n

6. p e a r

Copyright © Pearson Education, Inc., or its affiliates. All Rights Reserved.

Describing

Directions Circle the word that describes the place in each picture.

small (big)

dark (sunny)

Setting

Directions Circle the word that names the setting for each picture.

(school) bedroom

home (park)

Copyright © Pearson Education, Inc., or its affiliates. All Rights Reserved.

Nouns: Places

Directions Circle the places in each sentence.

1. I walk to (school).

2. I live in a (house).

3. The (park) is over there.

4. We swim in the (lake).

Directions Add a letter to make the nouns more than one.

5. room __s__   **7.** home __s__

6. building __s__   **8.** street __s__

Directions Draw a picture of a place you like to go. Write the name of the place.

9. Answers will vary. Accept

all reasonable answers.

Copyright © Pearson Education, Inc., or its affiliates. All Rights Reserved.

Produce Language

My Weekly Concept Journal

Directions Write your answers in the space provided.

Day 1 <u>Answers will vary.</u>

_____

Day 2 _____

_____

Day 3 _____

_____

Day 4 _____

_____

Copyright © Pearson Education, Inc., or its affiliates. All Rights Reserved.

Name _____

Produce Language

My Weekly Concept Journal

Directions Answer the weekly question.

Who is in our family?

Answers will vary but should show

understanding of the Concept Goals:

• recognize what a family is

• name the members of a family

• describe members of their own families

Copyright © Pearson Education, Inc., or its affiliates. All Rights Reserved.

Outside Our Door

Vocabulary

| bird | yellow | look |
| flowers | fun | outside |

Directions Match each word to its definition and picture.

1. bird — having the color of the sun or the middle part of an egg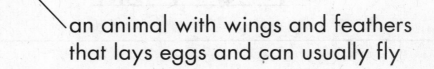

2. flowers — the brightly colored parts of a plant

3. yellow — an animal with wings and feathers that lays eggs and can usually fly

4. look — to turn your eyes toward something so that you can see it

Directions Finish the sentences. Use words from the box.

5. I like to play **outside** .

6. I saw a **bird** in a nest.

7. Telling riddles is **fun** .

Copyright © Pearson Education, Inc., or its affiliates. All Rights Reserved.

Name _____

The Sound /f/ Spelled *f*

Directions Look at each picture. Say the word. Write the word.

1.  f i s h

2.  f a n

3.  f o r k

The Sound /b/ Spelled *b*

Directions Look at the picture. Say the word. Write the word.

4. b a l l

5.  b i r d

6.  b e a r

Copyright © Pearson Education, Inc., or its affiliates. All Rights Reserved.

Name _____

Literary Analysis

Directions Look at these pictures. They are in the wrong order to tell a story. Write beginning, middle, or end below each of the pictures to tell the story.

_____ **middle**   _____ **end**   _____ **beginning**

Plot

Directions Draw three pictures that tell a story. Draw a picture that shows what happens at the beginning, middle, and end.

beginning	**middle**	**end**

Drawings will vary but should clearly have an order.

Copyright © Pearson Education, Inc., or its affiliates. All Rights Reserved.

Name _____

Verbs

Directions Circle the verbs.

1. Luis (walks) to the park.

2. Maria (plays) tag with friends.

3. Carlo (eats) lunch at school.

Directions Draw a line from each verb to the picture it matches.

4. runs

5. sleeps

6. sings

7. kicks

8. digs

9. eats

Copyright © Pearson Education, Inc., or its affiliates. All Rights Reserved.

Produce Language

My Weekly Concept Journal

Directions Write your answers in the space provided.

Day 1 <u>Answers will vary.</u>

_____
_____
_____
_____

Day 2 _____
_____
_____
_____

Day 3 _____
_____
_____
_____

Day 4 _____
_____
_____
_____

Copyright © Pearson Education, Inc., or its affiliates. All Rights Reserved.

Name _____

Produce Language

My Weekly Concept Journal

Directions Answer the weekly question.

What is outside our door?

<u>Answers will vary but should show</u>

<u>understanding of the Concept Goals:</u>

• <u>understand concepts about things that</u>

  <u>can be found outside</u>

• <u>name and describe objects that can be</u>

  <u>seen outside</u>

Copyright © Pearson Education, Inc., or its affiliates. All Rights Reserved.

Name _____

Neighborhood Friends

Vocabulary

dog	friendly	neighborhood
mail carrier	neighbor	two

Directions Match each word to its definition and picture.

1. dog   someone who lives near you

2. two   someone who delivers mail to people's houses

3. neighbor   an animal with four legs and a tail that is often kept as a pet

4. neighborhood   the small area of a town and the people who live there

5. mail carrier   the number 2

Directions Finish the sentences. Use words from the box.

6. I live in a pretty **neighborhood**.

7. The dog is very **friendly**.

Neighborhood Friends • Unit R, Week 4   **23**

Copyright © Pearson Education, Inc., or its affiliates. All Rights Reserved.

Name _____

The Sound /d/ Spelled *d*

Directions Look at each picture. Say the word. Write the word.

1.  d o g

2. d o l l

3. d o o r

The Sound /l/ Spelled *l, ll*

Directions Look at the picture. Say the word. Write the word.

4.  l i p s

5. d o l l

6.  h a l l

Copyright © Pearson Education, Inc., or its affiliates. All Rights Reserved.

Literary Analysis

Directions Look at the picture. Tell about the story.

1. _____
   __The story is__ not make-believe.

2. _____
   __The story is__ about a race.

Realism and Fantasy

Directions Circle the pictures that show a story is make-believe.

Copyright © Pearson Education, Inc., or its affiliates. All Rights Reserved.

Simple Sentences

Directions Finish the sentences using the words below.

I   the   like

1. We __**like**__ books.

2. __**I**__ ride my bike.

3. Lee takes __**the**__ bus home.

Directions Circle the letter in each sentence that should be a capital letter.

4. ⓣoday is my birthday.

5. ⓜy name is Ann.

6. ⓜark has a new bike.

Directions Look at each sentence below. What is missing? Add it to each sentence.

7. I like dogs __.__

8. This is my house __.__

9. Our neighbor is friendly __.__

Copyright © Pearson Education, Inc., or its affiliates. All Rights Reserved.

Produce Language

My Weekly Concept Journal

Directions Write your answers in the space provided.

Day 1 <u>Answers will vary.</u>

Day 2 _____

Day 3 _____

Day 4 _____

Copyright © Pearson Education, Inc., or its affiliates. All Rights Reserved.

Produce Language

My Weekly Concept Journal

Directions Answer the weekly question.

What can we do with our neighborhood friends?

Answers will vary but should show

understanding of the Concept Goals:

• recognize that friends can be found in

   a neighborhood

• name people found in a neighborhood

   and tell how we interact with them

• describe neighborhood friends

Copyright © Pearson Education, Inc., or its affiliates. All Rights Reserved.

Name _____

Around School

Vocabulary

backpack	teacher	he
classroom	read	

Directions Match each word to its definition and picture.

1. backpack   look at written words and understood their meaning

2. classroom   a bag that you carry on your back

3. read   someone whose job is to teach

4. teacher   a room in school where students are taught

Directions Finish the sentences. Use words from the box.

5. My lunch is in my **backpack** .

6. **He** is a good teacher.

7. The **classroom** is filled with desks.

Copyright © Pearson Education, Inc., or its affiliates. All Rights Reserved.

Name _____

The Sound /r/ Spelled *r*

Directions Look at each picture. Say the word. Write the word.

1. r i n g

2.  r o c k

3. r o p e

The Sound /w/ and the Sound /j/

Directions Circle the words that have the /w/ sound.
Draw a line under the words that have the /j/ sound.

(walk)    (window)

jump    <u>Jenna</u>

jug   (Will)

Copyright © Pearson Education, Inc., or its affiliates. All Rights Reserved.

Describing

Directions Circle the word that describes, or tells about, what is happening in each picture.

1. They (are swimming).

2. They (are cooking).

3. She (is sleeping).

Plot

Directions Look at the pictures. They tell a story. Complete these sentences about the plot.

4. In the beginning, <u>the kids made a large snowball</u>.

5. In the middle, <u>the kids put another snowball</u> . <u>on top</u>

6. In the end, <u>the kids made a snowman</u> .

Copyright © Pearson Education, Inc., or its affiliates. All Rights Reserved.

Name _____

Adjectives

Directions Circle the adjectives.

1. Mark has a (red) hat.

2. He has (three) pencils.

3. I climbed a (big) tree.

4. She has (two) sisters.

5. Maya has a (blue) backpack.

Directions Finish the sentences. Use the adjectives in the box.

big	two	yellow

6. Juan has a _____ **big** _____ dog.

7. I wore a _____ **yellow** _____ coat.

8. Tam gave me _____ **two** _____ crayons.

Answers may vary.

Copyright © Pearson Education, Inc., or its affiliates. All Rights Reserved.

Produce Language

My Weekly Concept Journal

Directions Write your answers in the space provided.

Day 1 <u>Answers will vary.</u>

Day 2

Day 3

Day 4

Copyright © Pearson Education, Inc., or its affiliates. All Rights Reserved.

Name _____

Produce Language

My Weekly Concept Journal

Directions Answer the weekly question.

What is around us at school?

Answers will vary but should show

understanding of the Concept Goals:

• recognize that certain objects and

  people can be found in a school

• provide examples of objects and people

  found at school

• name different things that children

  can do at school

Copyright © Pearson Education, Inc., or its affiliates. All Rights Reserved.

Around the Neighborhood

Vocabulary

fruit	buy	visit
vegetables	market	where

Directions Match each word to its definition and picture.

1. fruit —————— the part of a plant that has the seeds and is often sweet and good to eat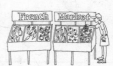

2. vegetables a place where people buy and sell goods

3. buy to get something by paying money for it

4. market plants, such as corn or potatoes, that are grown to be eaten

---

Directions Finish the sentences. Use words from the box.

5. I shop at the **market**.

6. I **visit** my aunt in the summer.

7. **Where** is Jorgé?

Copyright © Pearson Education, Inc., or its affiliates. All Rights Reserved.

Name _____

The Sound /v/ Spelled *v*

Directions Look at each picture. Say the word. Write the word.

1. v a s e

2. v a n

3. v i o l i n

The Sound /z/ Spelled *z, zz*

Directions Circle the words that have the /z/ sound.

  (zipper)

  books

 (zoo)

 (blizzard)

 shoe

 (pizza)

Copyright © Pearson Education, Inc., or its affiliates. All Rights Reserved.

Expressing Needs and Likes

Directions Tell if you **like** or **don't like** these things.

1. I _____ books.

2. I _____ strawberries.

3. I _____ spiders.

4. I _____ cats.

Answers will vary but will be *like* or *don't like*.

Realism and Fantasy

Directions Look at the picture. Is this story make-believe or could it happen?

5. The story is *make-believe* _____.

6. I know because *foxes don't wear clothes,*

foxes don't use magnifying glasses.

Copyright © Pearson Education, Inc., or its affiliates. All Rights Reserved.

Name _____

Sentences

Directions Circle the verbs in these sentences.

1. Sam (buys) fruit at the market.

2. The vegetables (are) fresh.

3. Mom (cut) the melon.

4. I (ate) an apple.

5. Dad (cooks) vegetable soup.

6. Juan (eats) carrots.

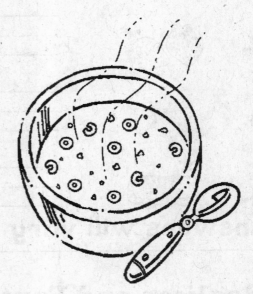

Directions Write a sentence about this picture.

---

7. **He eats an apple.**

Copyright © Pearson Education, Inc., or its affiliates. All Rights Reserved.

Produce Language

My Weekly Concept Journal

Directions Write your answers in the space provided.

Day 1 <u>Answers will vary.</u>

Day 2

Day 3

Day 4

Copyright © Pearson Education, Inc., or its affiliates. All Rights Reserved.

Name _____

Produce Language

My Weekly Concept Journal

Directions Answer the weekly question.

What can we see around our neighborhood?

Answers will vary but should show

understanding of the Concept Goals:

• understand the concepts about things

  we see in the neighborhood

• provide examples and describe objects

  in the neighborhood and at the market

Copyright © Pearson Education, Inc., or its affiliates. All Rights Reserved.

Animal Needs

Vocabulary

cat	slept	come	my
kitten	drank	pet	

Directions Match each word to its definition and picture.

1. cat   a young cat

2. kitten   rested with eyes closed

3. slept   swallowed liquid

4. drank   an animal that you take care of and keep at your home

5. pet   a small, furry animal that people often keep as a pet

---

Directions Finish the sentences. Use words from the box.

6. The cat _____drank_____ some water.

7. The dogs _____come_____ when I call them.

8. I like _____my_____ pets.

Copyright © Pearson Education, Inc., or its affiliates. All Rights Reserved.

The Sound /a/ Spelled a

Directions Look at each picture. Say the word. Write the word.

1. ____mad____

2.  ____cat____

3.  ____pan____

The Sound /k/ Spelled *ck*

Directions Look at the picture. Say the word. Write the word.

4.  ____duck____

5. ____sick____

6.  ____lock____

Copyright © Pearson Education, Inc., or its affiliates. All Rights Reserved.

Literary Analysis

Directions Circle the words that tell when.

1. They are swimming (now).

2. (Long ago), there were no cars.

3. We use computers (now).

4. (Now) we go into space.

5. Dinosaurs lived (long ago).

Character and Setting

Directions Circle the characters in the picture.
Then write where the story happens.

**circle all
the people**

The story happens __at the park__ .

Copyright © Pearson Education, Inc., or its affiliates. All Rights Reserved.

Name _____

Sentences

Directions Circle each letter that should be a capital letter.

1. (m)y dog is friendly.

2. (t)he cat had kittens.

3. (i)t slept on a rug.

4. (a) fish can be a pet.

5. (a)nimals need food.

Directions Look at each sentence. What is missing? Write it.

6. Paul likes animals _____

7. The puppy sleeps a lot _____

8. Cats like to play _____

9. The dog has a bone _____

10. I want a kitten _____

Copyright © Pearson Education, Inc., or its affiliates. All Rights Reserved.

Produce Language

My Weekly Concept Journal

Directions Write your answers in the space provided.

Day 1 <u>Answers will vary.</u>

Day 2

Day 3

Day 4

Copyright © Pearson Education, Inc., or its affiliates. All Rights Reserved.

Name _____

Produce Language

My Weekly Concept Journal

Directions Answer the weekly question.

What do pets need?

Answers will vary but should show

understanding of the Concept Goals:

• understand that pet animals need

   food, water, and a place to live

• describe what people do to help take

   care of pets

• recognize that pets depend on people

   for many of their needs

Copyright © Pearson Education, Inc., or its affiliates. All Rights Reserved.

Helping Animals

Vocabulary

sick	medicine	vet	want
examined	take	and	

Directions Match each word to its definition and picture.

1. sick

an animal doctor

2. examined

a substance given to help sick people get better

3. medicine

not healthy; having a disease

4. vet

looked at someone or something closely and carefully

Directions Finish the sentences. Use words from the box.

5. I ___**take**___ my dog to the park.

6. I ___**want**___ to take care of animals.

7. I took my cat ___**and**___ dog to the vet.

Copyright © Pearson Education, Inc., or its affiliates. All Rights Reserved.

Name _____

The Sound /i/ Spelled *i*

Directions Look at each picture. Say the word. Write the word.

1.  pin

2. wig

3. sit

The Sound /ks/ Spelled *x*

Directions Look at the picture. Say the word. Write the word.

4. fox

5.  box

6. six

Copyright © Pearson Education, Inc., or its affiliates. All Rights Reserved.

Comparing and Contrasting

Directions Tell about the pictures.

These hats are **alike**.
These balls are **different**.

Possible answers shown.

1. The hats are alike because <u>they look the same</u>.

2. The balls are different because <u>they are different shapes and sizes</u>.

Compare/Contrast Character, Plot, Setting

Directions Look at the pictures. Each tells a different story. Complete the sentences that tell how the stories are alike and different.

3. The stories are alike because <u>they are vets</u>.

4. The stories are different because <u>one vet is examining a lion. The other is examining a dog</u>.

Copyright © Pearson Education, Inc., or its affiliates. All Rights Reserved.

Subjects of Sentences

Directions Circle the subject of each sentence.

1. (The cat) is asleep.

2. (Dogs) like bones.

3. (A vet) helps animals.

4. (The dog) carries a bowl.

Directions Finish each sentence. Use a word from the box.

dog	cats	woman	vet

5. The _____cats_____ play with a ball of string.

6. The _____dog_____ has a bone.

7. The _____woman_____ took her pet to the vet.

8. The _____vet_____ helps sick animals.

Copyright © Pearson Education, Inc., or its affiliates. All Rights Reserved.

Produce Language

My Weekly Concept Journal

Directions Write your answers in the space provided.

Day 1 <u>Answers will vary.</u>

Day 2

Day 3

Day 4

Copyright © Pearson Education, Inc., or its affiliates. All Rights Reserved.

Produce Language

My Weekly Concept Journal

Directions   Answer the weekly question.

Who helps animals?

<u>Answers will vary but should show</u>

<u>understanding of the Concept Goals:</u>

- <u>recognize that veterinarians assist sick</u>

  <u>animals</u>

- <u>describe some of the ways that</u>

  <u>veterinarians help animals</u>

Copyright © Pearson Education, Inc., or its affiliates. All Rights Reserved.

Name _____

Animals That Help

Vocabulary

hiker	follow	rescue	help
woods	lost	scent	use

Directions Match each word to its definition and picture.

1. hiker

   the smell left behind by a person or animal

2. woods

   someone who takes a long walk in the country or in the mountains

3. follow

   to come or go after someone or something

4. rescue

   to save someone from danger

5. scent

   a small forest

Directions Finish the sentences. Use words from the box.

6. I _____**use**_____ my eyes to see.

7. I _____**lost**_____ my favorite toy.

8. Animals can _____**help**_____ people find their way.

Copyright © Pearson Education, Inc., or its affiliates. All Rights Reserved.

Name _____

The /o/ Sound Spelled *o*

Directions Look at each picture. Say the word. Write the word.

1.   hot

2.  log

3.  fox

Plurals with the Sound /z/ Spelled *s*

Directions Look at the picture. Say the word. Write the word.

4.  trees

5.  peas

6.  pigs

Copyright © Pearson Education, Inc., or its affiliates. All Rights Reserved.

Describing

Directions Circle the word that describes the animal in each sentence.

1. The dog is (friendly.)

2. The kitten is (small.)

3. The puppy is (black.)

4. The cat is (smart.)

5. The dragon is (big.)

Character and Setting

Directions Look at the picture. Complete these sentences about character and setting.

6. The characters are ____ **a boy** ____ and ____ **a dog** ____ .

7. The story happens ____ **outside** ____ .

Copyright © Pearson Education, Inc., or its affiliates. All Rights Reserved.

Name _____

Predicates of Sentences

Directions Circle the predicate of each sentence below.

1. The dog (gets the ball.)

2. The dog (licks the girl.)

3. The dog (plays outside.)

4. The dog (drinks water.)

5. The dog (has a stick.)

Directions Look at the pictures. Finish each sentence.
Write a predicate.

6.  The boy __reads a book__ .

7.  The girl __feeds the duck__ .

Copyright © Pearson Education, Inc., or its affiliates. All Rights Reserved.

Produce Language

My Weekly Concept Journal

Directions Write your answers in the space provided.

Day 1 <u>Answers will vary.</u>

Day 2

Day 3

Day 4

Copyright © Pearson Education, Inc., or its affiliates. All Rights Reserved.

Name _____

Produce Language

My Weekly Concept Journal

Directions Answer the weekly question.

How do animals help people?

Answers will vary but should show

understanding of the Concept Goals:

• recognize that animals can help people

• describe some of the specific ways in

  which animals assist people

 • learn vocabulary associated with

  rescue dogs

Copyright © Pearson Education, Inc., or its affiliates. All Rights Reserved.

Helping Wild Animals

Vocabulary

boats	ocean	clean	safe
dolphins	whales	protect	this

Directions Match each word to its definition and picture.

1. boats   not dirty

2. dolphins   very large area of water

3. clean   not in danger of being harmed or destroyed

4. ocean   gray sea animals with long pointed noses

5. safe   small ships that float in the water

Directions Finish the sentences. Use the words in the box.

6. We need to _____**protect**_____ animals from dirty water.

7. _____**Whales**_____ breathe through a hole on the top of their heads.

8. _____**This**_____ water is very clean.

Copyright © Pearson Education, Inc., or its affiliates. All Rights Reserved.

Name _____

Inflected Ending -s

Directions Add -s to each word. Write the new word on the line.

1.

eat

eats

2.

hit

hits

3.

kick

kicks

Inflected Ending -ing

Directions Add -ing to each word. Write the new word on the line.

4.

stand

standing

5.

carry

carrying

6.

jump

jumping

Copyright © Pearson Education, Inc., or its affiliates. All Rights Reserved.

Retelling

Directions Fill in each sentence with **is** or **was**.

1. Now: Mom _____**is**_____ cooking.

2. Already happened: Mom _____**was**_____ cooking.

3. Now: The boy _____**is**_____ running.

4. Already happened: The boy _____**was**_____ running.

5. Now: The girl _____**is**_____ reading.

6. Already happened: The girl _____**was**_____ reading.

Main Idea

Directions Look at the pictures. Tell what is happening.

7. The monkey is _____**eating**_____ .

8. They are _____**fishing**_____ .

9. They are _____**shopping**_____ .

Copyright © Pearson Education, Inc., or its affiliates. All Rights Reserved.

Name _____

Word Order

Directions Circle the name of the person or thing in each sentence. Draw a line under the words that tell something about the person or thing.

1. (Whales) need clean water.

2. (Boats) make water dirty.

3. (People) can protect dolphins.

Directions Put the words below together to make a sentence.

whales
live in the ocean

4. Whales live in the ocean.

cats
are good pets

5. Cats are good pets.

float on water
boats

6. Boats float on water.

Copyright © Pearson Education, Inc., or its affiliates. All Rights Reserved.

Produce Language

My Weekly Concept Journal

Directions Write your answers in the space provided.

Day 1 <u>Answers will vary.</u>

Day 2

Day 3

Day 4

Copyright © Pearson Education, Inc., or its affiliates. All Rights Reserved.

Produce Language

My Weekly Concept Journal

Directions Answer the weekly question.

How can we help wild animals?

Answers will vary but should show

understanding of the Concept Goals:

• recognize that some wild animals are

  in danger

• understand that people can help animals

  in the wild by protecting their homes

Copyright © Pearson Education, Inc., or its affiliates. All Rights Reserved.

Animals in Our Neighborhood

Vocabulary

branches	flying	tree
eggs	nest	

Directions Match each word to its definition and picture.

1. branches —————— parts of a tree that grow out from the middle

2. eggs — a large plant with branches, leaves, and a thick trunk

3. nest — a place made by a bird, insect, or small animal to live in

4. tree — round objects with hard shells that contain a baby bird

---

Directions Finish the sentences. Use words from the box.

5. I see birds _____**flying**_____ in the sky.

6. Birds rest on tree _____**branches**_____ .

7. There is a _____**nest**_____ in the tree.

Copyright © Pearson Education, Inc., or its affiliates. All Rights Reserved.

Name _____

The Sound /e/

Directions Look at each picture. Say the word. Write the word.

1. <u>**wet**</u>

2.  <u>**pen**</u>

3.  <u>**egg**</u>

Initial Consonant Blends

Directions Look at the picture. Say the word. Circle the letters that blend together to make the consonant sound at the beginning of the word.

4. **clock**

5.  **frog**

6. **drip**

Copyright © Pearson Education, Inc., or its affiliates. All Rights Reserved.

Retelling

Directions Read the sentences. Retell what happened using *and*.

The girl was sitting.
The girl was reading.

1. The girl was _____ **sitting** _____ and _____ **reading** _____ .

The boy was talking.
The boy was walking.

2. The boy was _____ **talking** _____ and _____ **walking** _____ .

The dog was eating.
The dog was drinking.

3. The dog was _____ **eating** _____ and _____ **drinking** _____ .

Main Idea

Directions Write what the sentences are all about.

The girls were at the beach.
They made sand castles.
They swam in the ocean.
They had fun.

The girls had fun at the beach.

Copyright © Pearson Education, Inc., or its affiliates. All Rights Reserved.

Name _____

Statements

Directions Circle the letters that should be capital letters.

1. (b)irds are wild animals.

2. (t)wo baby birds hatched.

3. (e)ggs have hard shells.

4. (b)irds eat worms.

5. (n)ests are safe places.

Directions What is missing? Add it to each sentence.

6. Birds lay eggs ____.

7. The baby bird was hungry ____.

8. Birds make nests ____.

9. Some birds sing ____.

10. There are eggs in that nest ____.

Copyright © Pearson Education, Inc., or its affiliates. All Rights Reserved.

Produce Language

My Weekly Concept Journal

Directions Write your answers in the space provided.

Day 1 Answers will vary.

Day 2

Day 3

Day 4

Copyright © Pearson Education, Inc., or its affiliates. All Rights Reserved.

Name _____

Produce Language

My Weekly Concept Journal

Directions Answer the weekly question.

Which wild animals live in our neighborhood?

Answers will vary but should show

understanding of the Concept Goals:

• recognize that wild animals can live in

  neighborhoods

• name places where wild animals can be

  be seen

• describe some of the characteristics

  of birds

Copyright © Pearson Education, Inc., or its affiliates. All Rights Reserved.

Name _____

Watching Animals

Vocabulary

| elephant | many | leads |
| herd | scientists | study |

Directions Match each word to its definition and picture.

1. elephant — people who work in science

2. herd — a group of animals of the same kind

3. scientists — to learn about a subject

4. study — a very large, gray animal with a long nose and big ears

Directions Finish the sentences. Use words from the box.

5. An **elephant** lives in a herd.

6. The mother elephant **leads** her babies to the river.

7. I have to **study** for the test.

Copyright © Pearson Education, Inc., or its affiliates. All Rights Reserved.

Name _____

The Sound /u/

Directions Look at each picture. Say the word. Write the word.

1.   rug

2.  bug

3.  tub

Final Consonant Blends

Directions Look at the picture. Say the word. Circle the letters that blend together to make the consonant sound at the end of the word.

4. la(mp)

5. ma(sk)

6. ju(mp)

Copyright © Pearson Education, Inc., or its affiliates. All Rights Reserved.

Name _____

Cause-and-Effect Relationship

Directions Look at the pictures. Tell what happened and why it happened.

1. The girl had to stay _____**inside**_____ because

it was _____**raining**_____ .

2. The boy got _____**dressed**_____ because it was

time to go to _____**school**_____ .

Cause and Effect

Directions Read the sentences. What happened? Why did it happen?

The bird got a worm because it was hungry.

3. The bird got a _____**worm**_____ .

4. It was _____**hungry**_____ .

Copyright © Pearson Education, Inc., or its affiliates. All Rights Reserved.

Name _____

Questions

Directions Look at each question below. What is missing?
Add it to each question.

1. What time is it __?__

2. When is the ball game __?__

3. Who is coming for dinner __?__

4. How many girls are in your class __?__

_____

Directions Circle the sentences that ask a question.

5. (How old are you?)

6. The ball is next to the tree.

7. (Where is my sock?)

8. (Will you read me a story?)

Copyright © Pearson Education, Inc., or its affiliates. All Rights Reserved.

Produce Language

My Weekly Concept Journal

Directions Write your answers in the space provided.

Day 1 <u>Answers will vary.</u>

Day 2

Day 3

Day 4

Copyright © Pearson Education, Inc., or its affiliates. All Rights Reserved.

Name _____

Produce Language

My Weekly Concept Journal

Directions Answer the weekly question.

What can we learn by watching wild animals?

Answers will vary but should show

understanding of the Concept Goals:

• understand that people can learn about

  wild animals by watching them

• describe what people have learned

  about elephants and how they live in

  the wild

Copyright © Pearson Education, Inc., or its affiliates. All Rights Reserved.

Name _____

Families

Vocabulary

family	**gather**	**think**
meal	**good**	**wash**

Directions Match each word to its definition and picture.

1. family — the food that you eat at one time

2. meal — to make something clean using water and soap

3. think — a group of people who are related to each other

4. wash — to use your mind to decide something, have ideas, or solve problems

Directions Finish the sentences. Use words from the box.

5. The meal Mom made was __**good**__ .

6. We __**gather**__ together at dinner time.

7. I help __**wash**__ the dishes.

Copyright © Pearson Education, Inc., or its affiliates. All Rights Reserved.

Name _____

The Digraphs /sh/ and /th/

Directions Look at each picture. Say the word. Write the word.

1.   __**sh**__ oe

2.  fi __**sh**__

3. ba __**th**__

The Sound /ȯ/ in *Ball*

Directions Look at the picture. Say the word. Write the word.

4. **fall**

5. **ball**

6. **mall**

Copyright © Pearson Education, Inc., or its affiliates. All Rights Reserved.

Retelling

Directions Circle the words that tell about things that happened.

1. We (were baking) a cake.

2. He (was washing) the dog.

3. She (was brushing) her teeth.

4. They (were skating.)

Main Idea and Details

Directions Look at the picture. Read the sentences. Circle the main idea. Draw a line under the detail.

(José and his mom were planting a tree.)

They were wearing gloves.

Copyright © Pearson Education, Inc., or its affiliates. All Rights Reserved.

Name _____

Nouns

Directions Circle the nouns.

1. (Roberta) likes to cook.

2. The (meal) is good.

3. The (dish) is hot.

4. The (family) cooks together.

5. This is my (house.)

Directions Finish the sentences. Use the nouns in the box.

boy	game	grass

6. We were playing ball on the ___**grass**___.

7. We were playing a good ___**game**___.

8. The ___**boy**___ is walking the dog.

Copyright © Pearson Education, Inc., or its affiliates. All Rights Reserved.

Produce Language

My Weekly Concept Journal

Directions Write your answers in the space provided.

Day 1 <u>Answers will vary.</u>

Day 2

Day 3

Day 4

Copyright © Pearson Education, Inc., or its affiliates. All Rights Reserved.

Name _____

Produce Language

My Weekly Concept Journal

Directions Answer the weekly question.

What does a family do together?

Answers will vary but should show

understanding of the Concept Goals:

• understand that families are communities

• name ways that families work and play

  together

• describe ways in which family members

  work together

Copyright © Pearson Education, Inc., or its affiliates. All Rights Reserved.

At School

Vocabulary

janitor	be	principal
nurse	make	

Directions Match each word to its definition and picture.

1. janitor — to create something or put something together

2. nurse — someone who is trained to take care of people who are sick or injured

3. make — someone who is in charge of a school

4. principal — someone who cleans a building and repairs things in it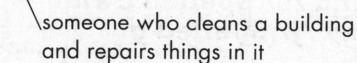

Directions Finish the sentences. Use words from the box.

5. I _____**make**_____ new friends at school.

6. I go to the school _____**nurse**_____ if I feel sick.

7. I want to _____**be**_____ a teacher.

Copyright © Pearson Education, Inc., or its affiliates. All Rights Reserved.

Name _____

Long *a* Spelled *a_e*

Directions Look at each picture. Say the word. Write the word.

1.  c __a__ n __e__

2.  t __a__ p __e__

3.  sn __a__ k __e__

4.  g __a__ m __e__

The Sound /s/ Spelled *c* and the Sound /j/ Spelled *g*

Directions Look at the picture. Say the word. Write the word.

5.  **mice**

6. **race**

7. **cage**

Copyright © Pearson Education, Inc., or its affiliates. All Rights Reserved.

Cause-and-Effect Relationship

Directions Read each sentence. Circle what happened.
Underline why it happened.

1. (The bell rang) because <u>it was time for lunch.</u>

2. (I put away my books) because <u>it was time to go home.</u>

3. (Jack waited in line) because <u>it was not his turn.</u>

4. (I sharpened my pencil) because <u>the tip broke.</u>

Cause and Effect

Directions Finish the sentences. Tell why. Use **because.**

5. I walk to school **because I live one block away.** .

6. Anna went to the nurse **because she felt sick.** .

7. The janitor cleaned the floor **because it was dirty.** .

Answers will vary. Sample answers shown.

Copyright © Pearson Education, Inc., or its affiliates. All Rights Reserved.

Name _____

Proper Nouns

Directions Circle the proper nouns.

1. Our nurse is (Mrs. Cruz).

2. I live in (California).

3. We drove across the (Golden Gate Bridge).

4. Our house is on (Oak Lane).

Directions Match the proper nouns to the pictures.

5. Grandma Betty

6. Dr. Smith

7. United States

8. Statue of Liberty

Copyright © Pearson Education, Inc., or its affiliates. All Rights Reserved.

Produce Language

My Weekly Concept Journal

Directions Write your answers in the space provided.

Day 1 <u>Answers will vary.</u>

Day 2

Day 3

Day 4

Copyright © Pearson Education, Inc., or its affiliates. All Rights Reserved.

Name _____

Produce Language

My Weekly Concept Journal

Directions Answer the weekly question.

How is a school a community?

Answers will vary but should show

understanding of the Concept Goals:

• recognize that students and school

  workers form a community at school

• name jobs that people do in a school

Copyright © Pearson Education, Inc., or its affiliates. All Rights Reserved.

Community Workers

Vocabulary

litter	playground	nice
people	fixed	

Directions Match each word to its definition and picture.

1. litter

more than one person

2. people

repaired something

3. playground

a small area of land where children play

4. fixed

waste paper and other things that people leave on the ground in public

---

Directions Finish the sentences. Use words from the box.

5. I live in a _____ **nice** _____ community.

6. _____ **People** _____ care about our community.

7. I like to go to the **playground** .

Copyright © Pearson Education, Inc., or its affiliates. All Rights Reserved.

Name _____

Long *i* Spelled *i_e*

Directions Look at each picture. Say the word. Write the word.

 1.   t i r e

 2.   sm i l e

 3.   m i c e

---

The Sounds /hw/ and /ch/

Directions Look at the picture. Say the word. Write the word.

 4.   **whale**

5.   **cheese**

 6.   **watch**

Copyright © Pearson Education, Inc., or its affiliates. All Rights Reserved.

Asking Questions

Directions Read each sentence. Circle the words **What is** and **What are.**

1. (What is) your name?

2. (What are) you doing?

3. (What are) they playing?

4. (What is) he making?

5. (What is) that?

Author's Purpose

Directions Read the sign. Tell why you think the author wrote it.

6. The author wrote the sign **to tell everyone to**

pick up their trash.

Answers may vary.

Copyright © Pearson Education, Inc., or its affiliates. All Rights Reserved.

Special Titles

Directions Circle the title in each name.

1. (Mrs.) Diaz

2. (Doctor) Tan

3. (Ms.) Wells

4. (Judge) Reyes

5. (Mr.) Lee

Directions Write a different title in front of each name.

6. _____ Cabot

7. _____ Young

8. _____ Goodman

9. _____ Levin

Answers will vary but may include Mr., Mrs., Ms., Doctor, Principal, or Officer.

Copyright © Pearson Education, Inc., or its affiliates. All Rights Reserved.

Produce Language

My Weekly Concept Journal

Directions Write your answers in the space provided.

Day 1 <u>Answers will vary.</u>

Day 2

Day 3

Day 4

Copyright © Pearson Education, Inc., or its affiliates. All Rights Reserved.

Produce Language

My Weekly Concept Journal

Directions Answer the weekly question.

Who works to make our community a nice place?

Answers will vary but should show

understanding of the Concept Goals:

• recognize that communities need to be

taken care of

• name some of the things people do to

keep their communities nice

Copyright © Pearson Education, Inc., or its affiliates. All Rights Reserved.

Animal Communities

Vocabulary

hole	**meerkats**	**inside**
ground	**communities**	**under**

Directions Match each word to its definition and picture.

1. hole ——————————— an open space in the ground

2. ground — the inner part of something

3. meerkats — small African animals that have grey coats, stand near their homes, and live in groups

4. inside — in or to a lower place that is below something

5. under — the surface of the Earth

Directions Finish the sentences. Use words from the box.

6. I hid **under** a table in the house.

7. **Meerkats** live in a hole.

8. Some animals live in **communities**.

Copyright © Pearson Education, Inc., or its affiliates. All Rights Reserved.

Name _____

Long *o* Spelled *o_e*

Directions Look at each picture. Write the word. Say the word.

1. ____**hole**____

2. ____**rope**____

3. ____**bone**____

4. ____**cone**____

Contractions *n't*, *'m*, and *'ll*

Directions Match the contraction with the words.

5. __C__ can't   **A.** we will

6. __A__ we'll   **B.** I am

7. __B__ I'm   **C.** can not

Copyright © Pearson Education, Inc., or its affiliates. All Rights Reserved.

Sequencing

Directions Write about what you do at bedtime.

_____

1. First, I **put on pajamas** .

_____

2. Next, I **brush my teeth** .

_____

3. Last, I **get in bed** .

Answers will vary. Sample answers shown.

Sequence

Directions These pictures are not in order. Label what happens **first**, **next**, and **last**.

José's plant grows.

_____
last

José plants seeds.

_____
first

José waters the seeds.

_____
next

Copyright © Pearson Education, Inc., or its affiliates. All Rights Reserved.

Name _____

Proper Nouns

Directions Write the names of two people. Use a capital letter at the start of each name.

1. _____

2. _____

Answers will vary. Accept all reasonable answers.

Directions Write the names of three months. Use a capital letter at the start of each name.

3. _____

4. _____

5. _____

Answers will vary. Accept all reasonable answers.

Directions Circle the proper nouns that are *not* capitalized.

6. I want to play with (jane).

7. Meerkats live in (africa).

8. My birthday is on (april) fifth.

Copyright © Pearson Education, Inc., or its affiliates. All Rights Reserved.

Produce Language

My Weekly Concept Journal

Directions Write your answers in the space provided.

Day 1 <u>Answers will vary.</u>

Day 2

Day 3

Day 4

Copyright © Pearson Education, Inc., or its affiliates. All Rights Reserved.

Name _____

Produce Language

My Weekly Concept Journal

Directions Answer the weekly question.

How do animal communities work together to survive?

Answers will vary but should show

understanding of the Concept Goals:

• recognize that meerkats and other animals

live in communities to help them survive

• name things that meerkats do in their

communities

• describe ways in which meerkats help each

other survive

Copyright © Pearson Education, Inc., or its affiliates. All Rights Reserved.

Plant and Animal Communities

Vocabulary

chain	grass	these
food	strong	

Directions Match each word to its definition and picture.

1. chain

2. food

3. grass

4. strong

5. these

the ones here; the ones nearer than that one

a common plant with thin, green leaves that covers land

what you eat

a group of things joined together

having a lot of power or force

Directions Finish the sentences. Use words from the box.

6. The _____**grass**_____ is long and green.

7. _____**These**_____ cows are eating.

8. They will grow _____**strong**_____.

Copyright © Pearson Education, Inc., or its affiliates. All Rights Reserved.

Name _____

Long *u* Spelled *u_e* and Long *e* Spelled *e_e*

Directions Circle the word in each pair with the long *e* sound.

1. (Pete)   pet

2. ever   (eve)

3. (these)   them

Directions Circle the word in each pair with the long *u* sound.

4. (tune)   cut

5. (cute)   nut

6. put   (huge)

Inflected Ending *-ed*

Directions Add *-ed* to each word. Write the new word.

7.

laugh

laughed

8.

jump

jumped

9.

walk

walked

Copyright © Pearson Education, Inc., or its affiliates. All Rights Reserved.

Describing

Directions Read each sentence. Circle the word that describes.

1. The cows are (brown.)

2. The grass is (green.)

3. Milk is (white.)

4. A fly is (small.)

Author's Purpose

Directions Read the list of book titles. Match each title to the picture that shows what it can teach us about.

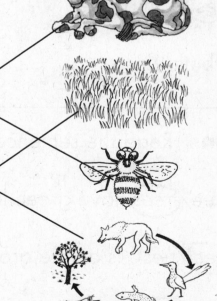

5. All About Bees

6. The Food Chain

7. Cows and Bulls

8. How Grass Grows

Copyright © Pearson Education, Inc., or its affiliates. All Rights Reserved.

Name _____

Singular and Plural Nouns

Directions Add -s to the end of each singular noun to make it plural.

1. cow __s__

2. bird __s__

3. nest __s__

4. tree __s__

Directions Circle the singular nouns. Underline the plural nouns.

5. The <u>cows</u> are big.

6. The (nest) is in a (tree)

7. <u>Birds</u> build <u>nests</u>.

Directions Read the sentences. Circle the correct noun.

8. The tree/(trees) have green leaves.

9. The (nest)/nests is on the ground.

10. Cow/(Cows) eat grass.

Copyright © Pearson Education, Inc., or its affiliates. All Rights Reserved.

Produce Language

My Weekly Concept Journal

Directions Write your answers in the space provided.

Day 1 <u>Answers will vary.</u>

Day 2

Day 3

Day 4

Copyright © Pearson Education, Inc., or its affiliates. All Rights Reserved.

Name _____

Produce Language

My Weekly Concept Journal

Directions Answer the weekly question.

How are plant and animal communities important to each other?

<u>Answers will vary but should show a basic</u>

<u>understanding of the Concept Goals:</u>

• <u>understand how plant and animal</u>

<u>communities are important to each other</u>

• <u>tell how plants and animals share space</u>

<u>and give each other food</u>

• <u>explain a simple food chain</u>

Copyright © Pearson Education, Inc., or its affiliates. All Rights Reserved.

Insect Communities

Vocabulary

bees	queen	return
hive	insects	some

Directions Match each word to its definition and picture.

1. queen

flying insects that make honey and can sting you

2. bees

a place where bees live

3. insects

the female ruler of a country or other area

4. hive

bugs that have six legs, such as flies

Directions Finish the sentences. Use words from the box.

5. The _____**queen**_____ bee lays eggs.

6. _____**Some**_____ bees leave the hive.

7. They _____**return**_____ to make honey.

Copyright © Pearson Education, Inc., or its affiliates. All Rights Reserved.

Name _____

Long e Spelled *e, ee*

Directions Look at each picture. Say the word. Finish the word.

1.  b __e__ __e__

2.  kn __e__ __e__

3.  tr __e__ __e__

4.  t __e__ __e__ th

Directions Say each word. Circle the ones that have the long e sound.

ⓜⓔⓔⓣ meet   set   her

Ⓗⓔ He   ⓈⒽⒺ she   when

Syllables VCCV

Directions Look at the picture. Say the word. Draw a line to show the two syllables.

5.  rab|bit

6.  pic|nic

7.  bas|ket

Copyright © Pearson Education, Inc., or its affiliates. All Rights Reserved.

Comparing

Directions Look at each picture. Complete the sentences that tell how the things are the same.

An ant is an insect.
A bee is an insect.

1. Both are _____insects_____.

A ball is round.
A wheel is round.

2. Both are _____round_____.

Compare and Contrast

Directions Look at each picture. Complete the sentences that tell how the things are different.

3. Ice is _____cold_____.

4. Fire is _____hot_____.

Copyright © Pearson Education, Inc., or its affiliates. All Rights Reserved.

Name _____

Nouns in Sentences

Directions Circle the nouns in the sentences.

1. (Bees) can fly.

2. (Insects) live together like (people) do.

3. There is a (hive) on the (tree).

4. The (family) plays a (game).

Directions Finish each sentence. Use the nouns in the box.

tree	eggs	street
people	bees	

5. _____**Bees**_____ live in a hive.

6. There is a hive on that _____**tree**_____.

7. The queen bee lays _____**eggs**_____.

8. _____**People**_____ live in towns.

9. My house is on that _____**street**_____.

Copyright © Pearson Education, Inc., or its affiliates. All Rights Reserved.

Produce Language

My Weekly Concept Journal

Directions Write your answers in the space provided.

Day 1 <u>Answers will vary.</u>

Day 2

Day 3

Day 4

Copyright © Pearson Education, Inc., or its affiliates. All Rights Reserved.

Name _____

Produce Language

My Weekly Concept Journal

Directions Answer the weekly question.

How is an insect community like a community of people?

Answers will vary but should show a basic

understanding of the Concept Goals:

• recognize that insects live together in

  communities

• name some of the jobs that bees do in

  their communities

• compare and contrast insect

  communities and communities of people

Copyright © Pearson Education, Inc., or its affiliates. All Rights Reserved.

Changing Places

Vocabulary

building	things	land
always	torn	stands

Directions Match each word to its definition and picture.

1. building   ground or surface of the Earth

2. things   objects

3. torn   pulled apart by force

4. land   something with a roof and walls such as a house, office, or church

5. stands   is upright in a certain place

Directions Finish the sentences. Use words from the box.

6. The old house was _____**torn**_____ down.

7. I live in a new ____**building**____.

8. I have ____**always**____ lived here.

Copyright © Pearson Education, Inc., or its affiliates. All Rights Reserved.

Long *i* and Long *e* Spelled *y*

Directions Look at each picture. Say the word. Write the word.

1. _____ **fly** _____

2.  _____ **city** _____

3. _____ **family** _____

4.  _____ **sky** _____

Long Vowels *e*, *i*, and *o*

Directions Finish the words. Add a vowel from the box.

e	i	o

5. g __o__

6. h __i/e__

7. m __e__

8. s __o__

9. sh __e__

Copyright © Pearson Education, Inc., or its affiliates. All Rights Reserved.

Sequencing

Directions Circle the words that tell when things happen.

1. (At first), the land was a farm.

2. (Now), there is a building on the land.

3. (At first), my family lived in a big city.

4. (Now), my family lives in a small town.

Sequence

Directions Look at the pictures. Add **At first** or **Now** to each sentence to tell the order.

5. ___At first___, Leo was hungry.

6. ___Now___, he is eating lunch.

7. ___At first___, there was a snowman.

8. ___Now___, the snowman has melted.

Copyright © Pearson Education, Inc., or its affiliates. All Rights Reserved.

Action Verbs

Directions Circle the action verbs.

1. He (runs) to school.

2. They (play) tag.

3. The cat (chases) a mouse.

4. The bird (builds) a nest.

5. The tree (grows) tall.

Directions Complete the sentences using these action verbs.
mows   eat   jump   run

6. I _____**jump**_____ rope.

7. We _____**eat**_____ lunch.

8. They _____**run**_____ a race.

9. He _____**mows**_____ the grass.

Copyright © Pearson Education, Inc., or its affiliates. All Rights Reserved.

Produce Language

My Weekly Concept Journal

Directions Write your answers in the space provided.

Day 1 <u>Answers will vary.</u>

_____
_____
_____

Day 2 _____

_____
_____
_____

Day 3 _____

_____
_____
_____

Day 4 _____

_____
_____
_____

Copyright © Pearson Education, Inc., or its affiliates. All Rights Reserved.

Name _____

Produce Language

My Weekly Concept Journal

Directions Answer the weekly question.

How do places change?

<u>Answers will vary but should show</u>
<u>understanding of the Concept Goals:</u>
<u>• recognize that a place can change</u>
<u>• discuss ways in which the land and</u>
  <u>buildings can change</u>

Copyright © Pearson Education, Inc., or its affiliates. All Rights Reserved.

People Changing

Vocabulary

| bicycle | continue | riding |
| wheels | every | sure |

Directions Match each word to its definition and picture.

1. bicycle   each one

2. wheels   a vehicle with two wheels that you sit on and ride

3. every   the round things under a vehicle that turn around and around and allow it to move

4. riding ————— being carried on an animal or on a bicycle

Directions Finish the sentences. Use words from the box.

5. I am _____ **sure** _____ that I have the best bicycle.

6. I ride it _____ **every** _____ day.

7. I stop, but my friends _____ **continue** _____ to go.

Copyright © Pearson Education, Inc., or its affiliates. All Rights Reserved.

The Sounds /ng/ and /ngk/

Directions Look at each picture. Say the word. Write the word.

1. 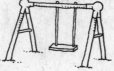 _____ **sink** _____

2. _____ **swing** _____

3. _____ **bank** _____

4. _____ **ring** _____

Using Compound Words

Directions Look at the pictures. Put the two words together to make a new word.

5. bed + room **bedroom**

6.   camp + fire **campfire**

7.  sea + shell **seashell**

Copyright © Pearson Education, Inc., or its affiliates. All Rights Reserved.

Describing Action

Directions Circle the action words.

1. Anna (rode) her bike to the park.

2. The puppy (grew) into a big dog.

3. They (walked) to school together.

4. We (sang) the song "Happy Birthday."

Plot

Directions Read the story. Answer the questions.

A boy lost his puppy. A girl found the puppy.
The boy was happy to have his pet back.

5. What is the problem in the story?

The puppy was _____**lost**_____.

6. How was the problem solved?

A girl _____**found**_____ it.

Copyright © Pearson Education, Inc., or its affiliates. All Rights Reserved.

Name _____

Verbs That Add -s

Directions Circle the correct verb in each sentence.

1. She *play*/*plays* with her toys.

2. They *walk*/*walks* home after school.

3. He *run*/*runs* very fast.

4. The ball *roll*/*rolls* down the hill.

5. He *pack*/*packs* his bag for a trip.

Directions Add -*s* to these verbs. Then use them to complete the sentences.

change _____
learn _____
talk _____

6. He _____**talks**_____ to his friend.

7. She _____**learns**_____ how to write.

8. He _____**changes**_____ the tire.

Copyright © Pearson Education, Inc., or its affiliates. All Rights Reserved.

Produce Language

My Weekly Concept Journal

Directions Write your answers in the space provided.

Day 1 <u>Answers will vary.</u>

_____

_____

_____

_____

Day 2 _____

_____

_____

_____

_____

Day 3 _____

_____

_____

_____

_____

Day 4 _____

_____

_____

_____

_____

Copyright © Pearson Education, Inc., or its affiliates. All Rights Reserved.

Name _____

Produce Language

My Weekly Concept Journal

Directions Answer the weekly question.

What do we learn as we grow and change?

<u>Answers will vary but should show</u>
<u>understanding of the Concept Goals:</u>
- <u>understand ways in which people</u>
  <u>change as they grow</u>
- <u>name different things that children</u>
  <u>learn as they grow</u>

Copyright © Pearson Education, Inc., or its affiliates. All Rights Reserved.

Exciting Changes

Vocabulary

house	soccer	friends
school	our	scared

Directions Match each word to its definition and picture.

1. house — a game in which players try to kick a ball between two posts

2. school — a place where children go to learn

3. soccer — made someone feel afraid

4. friends — a building that you live in, especially with your family

5. scared — people whom you like and trust very much

Directions Finish the sentences. Use words from the box.

6. There is a park near my **house or school**.

7. I go there to play _____ **soccer** _____.

8. _____ **Our** _____ new friends are very nice.

Copyright © Pearson Education, Inc., or its affiliates. All Rights Reserved.

Name _____

Ending -es

Directions Write each word. Then add -es.

1.  **boxes**

2.  **benches**

3.  **foxes**

The Sound /ôr/ Spelled *or, ore*

Directions Look at the picture. Say the word. Write the word.

4.  **corn**

5.  **fork**

6. 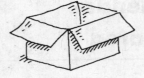 **store**

Copyright © Pearson Education, Inc., or its affiliates. All Rights Reserved.

Defining

Directions Finish the sentences. Use the words in the box.

fruit	sport	building

1. An apple is a ___**fruit**___ .

2. A school is a ___**building**___ .

3. Soccer is a ___**sport**___ .

4. Baseball is a ___**sport**___ .

5. A house is a ___**building**___ .

6. A banana is a ___**fruit**___ .

Classify and Categorize

Directions Complete the sentences that tell how two things are alike.

7. An apple and a banana are ___**fruits**___ .

8. A school and a house are ___**buildings**___ .

9. Soccer and baseball are ___**sports**___ .

Copyright © Pearson Education, Inc., or its affiliates. All Rights Reserved.

Name _____

Verbs That Do Not Add -s

Directions Circle the correct verb in each sentence.

1. The children (play)/plays games.

2. My grandparents (move)/moves to a new house.

3. The brothers (run)/runs very fast.

4. Mom and I (walk)/walks to school together.

5. They (put)/puts the toys into boxes.

Directions Finish each sentence. Use a verb from the box.

| walk | kick | write | ride | jump |

6. The players _____**kick**_____ the soccer ball.

7. The girls _____**jump**_____ rope.

8. The students _____**write**_____ their names on the paper.

9. My friends _____**walk**_____ to school with me.

10. We _____**ride**_____ our bikes to the park.

Copyright © Pearson Education, Inc., or its affiliates. All Rights Reserved.

Produce Language

My Weekly Concept Journal

Directions Write your answers in the space provided.

Day 1 <u>Answers will vary.</u> _____

_____

_____

_____

Day 2 _____

_____

_____

_____

_____

Day 3 _____

_____

_____

_____

_____

Day 4 _____

_____

_____

_____

_____

Copyright © Pearson Education, Inc., or its affiliates. All Rights Reserved.

Name _____

Produce Language

My Weekly Concept Journal

Directions Answer the weekly question.

How can change be exciting?

<u>Answers will vary but should show</u>
<u>understanding of the Concept Goals:</u>
<u>• understand the concept of excitement</u>
<u>• recognize that change can be a good</u>
<u> thing and discuss ways in which change</u>
<u> is good</u>

Copyright © Pearson Education, Inc., or its affiliates. All Rights Reserved.

Weather Changes

Vocabulary

cloudy	again	soon
rain	drops	weather

Directions Match each word to its definition and picture.

1. cloudy   small amounts of liquid

2. rain   having a dark sky, full of clouds

3. drops   drops of water that fall from the sky

4. weather————— the temperature and conditions
          such as wind, rain, or sun

Directions Finish the sentences. Use words from the box.

5. Is it going to rain **again or soon** ?

6. ____**Rain**____ helps flowers grow.

7. It is going to snow **again or soon**.

Copyright © Pearson Education, Inc., or its affiliates. All Rights Reserved.

Name _____

Endings -ed and -ing

Directions Add *-ing* or *-ed* to each verb. Remember to double the last consonant of the base word. Write the new word.

1.   run + ing **running**

2. 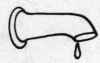   drip + ed **dripped**

3.   spin + ing **spinning**

4.    shop + ed **shopped**

The Sound /är/

Directions Look at the picture. Say the word. Write the word.

5.    **car**

6.   **party**

7.   **star**

Copyright © Pearson Education, Inc., or its affiliates. All Rights Reserved.

Sequencing

Directions What did you do this morning? Write sentences. Use **first, next,** and **last.**

1. First, I **got out of bed** .

2. Next, I **got dressed** .

3. Last, I **brushed my teeth** .

Answers will vary. Sample answers shown.

Sequence

Directions These pictures are not in order. Put them in order. Write **1, 2,** and **3.**

Last, the sun comes up. __3__

First, it is dark. __1__

Next, it starts to get light. __2__

Copyright © Pearson Education, Inc., or its affiliates. All Rights Reserved.

Name _____

Verbs for Present and for Past

Directions Circle the verbs. Write **now** or **past** on the line to tell when it happened.

1. It ⟨rained⟩ yesterday. _____**past**_____

2. She ⟨plays⟩ with her friends. _____**now**_____

3. The cat ⟨jumps⟩ onto the chair. _____**now**_____

4. We ⟨baked⟩ a cake. _____**past**_____

5. My grandparents ⟨called⟩ me on the
phone. _____**past**_____

Directions Circle the correct verb.

6. It *rains*/⟨*rained*⟩ last night.

7. Now, she ⟨*plays*⟩/*played* outside.

8. He *picks*/⟨*picked*⟩ apples yesterday.

9. She *brushes*/⟨*brushed*⟩ her teeth last night.

10. Now, the sun ⟨*shines*⟩/*shined*.

Copyright © Pearson Education, Inc., or its affiliates. All Rights Reserved.

Produce Language

My Weekly Concept Journal

Directions Write your answers in the space provided.

Day 1 <u>Answers will vary.</u>

_____

_____

_____

_____

Day 2 _____

_____

_____

_____

_____

Day 3 _____

_____

_____

_____

Day 4 _____

_____

_____

_____

_____

Copyright © Pearson Education, Inc., or its affiliates. All Rights Reserved.

Name _____

Produce Language

My Weekly Concept Journal

Directions Answer the weekly question.

How does weather change?

Answers will vary but should show
understanding of the Concept Goals:
• recognize that weather can change
• describe changes in the weather
• explain how raindrops form in clouds

_____
_____
_____
_____
_____
_____
_____
_____
_____
_____
_____
_____
_____
_____
_____

Copyright © Pearson Education, Inc., or its affiliates. All Rights Reserved.

The Seasons

Vocabulary

birds	**push**	**wait**
bloom	**spring**	

Directions Match each word to its definition and picture.

1. birds———— animals with wings and feathers that lay eggs and usually can fly

2. bloom the season between winter and summer

3. push to stay in place until something happens

4. spring to move with a force

5. wait to make flowers

Directions Finish the sentences. Use words from the box.

6. My favorite season is _____ **spring** _____.

7. That is when flowers _____ **bloom** _____.

8. I see _____ **birds** _____ building a nest.

Copyright © Pearson Education, Inc., or its affiliates. All Rights Reserved.

Name _____

The Sound /ėr/ Spelled *er, ir, ur*

Directions Circle the word that matches each picture.

1.   (bird)   bind

2.   gill   (girl)

3.  safe   (surf)

4.   (shirt)   ships

Contractions *'s, 've,* and *'re*

Directions Put the words together. Write the contraction.

5. he + is _____**he's**_____

6. you + have _____**you've**_____

7. they + are _____**they're**_____

8. I + have _____**I've**_____

9. what + is _____**what's**_____

10. we + are _____**we're**_____

Copyright © Pearson Education, Inc., or its affiliates. All Rights Reserved.

Defining

Directions Finish the sentences. Use these words:
plant   animal

1.   A flower is a _____**plant**_____ .

2.   A dog is an _____**animal**_____ .

3.   A tree is a _____**plant**_____ .

Classify and Categorize

Directions Circle the two things that belong to the same group. Then finish the sentence.

The _____**apple**_____ and the _____**banana**_____ belong to the same group.

The _____**butterfly**_____ and the _____**bee**_____ belong to the same group.

Copyright © Pearson Education, Inc., or its affiliates. All Rights Reserved.

Name _____

Verbs

Directions Finish the sentences. Use the verbs in the box. You will use one verb two times.

am	**is**	**were**
was	**are**	

1. Now   They _____**are**_____ walking.

2. Past   They _____**were**_____ walking.

3. Now   I _____**am**_____ talking.

4. Past   I _____**was**_____ talking.

5. Now   He _____**is**_____ running.

6. Past   He _____**was**_____ running.

Directions Choose the correct verb. Write it on the line.

7. Last week, the flowers _____**were**_____ in bloom. *(are, were)*

8. Yesterday _____**was**_____ rainy. *(is, was)*

9. Today _____**is**_____ sunny. *(is, was)*

Copyright © Pearson Education, Inc., or its affiliates. All Rights Reserved.

Produce Language

My Weekly Concept Journal

Directions Write your answers in the space provided.

Day 1 <u>Answers will vary.</u>_____

_____

_____

_____

Day 2 _____

_____

_____

_____

Day 3 _____

_____

_____

_____

Day 4 _____

_____

_____

_____

Copyright © Pearson Education, Inc., or its affiliates. All Rights Reserved.

Name _____

Produce Language

My Weekly Concept Journal

Directions Answer the weekly question.

What happens as the seasons change?

Answers will vary but should show
understanding of the Concept Goals:
- recognize that each year has four
  seasons
- name the four seasons
- describe things that happen specifically
  in the spring

_____

_____

_____

_____

_____

_____

_____

_____

_____

_____

_____

_____

Copyright © Pearson Education, Inc., or its affiliates. All Rights Reserved.

Name _____

Animal Changes

Vocabulary

geese	migrate	sea turtle
before	south	won't

Directions Match each word to its definition and picture.

1. geese

to move from one place to another to live or find work

2. migrate

the direction that is opposite of north

3. south

birds with long necks that are related to ducks

4. sea turtle

an animal with a hard shell that lives mainly in the water

Directions Finish the sentences. Use words from the box.

5. Some animals __**migrate**__ before winter.

6. __**Geese**__ fly south.

7. We won't see them __**before**__ the summer.

Copyright © Pearson Education, Inc., or its affiliates. All Rights Reserved.

Name _____

Comparative Endings -er and -est

Directions Add -er or -est to each word. Write the new word on the line.

1.   small + er = __smaller__

2.  fast + est = __fastest__

Directions Add -er or -est to each word. Remember to double the last consonant of the base word. Write the new word.

3.   big + est = __biggest__

4.   hot + er = __hotter__

The Sound /j/ Spelled *dge*

Directions Look at the picture. Say the word. Write the word.

5.   __bridge__

6.   __judge__

Copyright © Pearson Education, Inc., or its affiliates. All Rights Reserved.

Sequencing

Directions Look at the pictures. Finish the sentences.
Use these words: **before   after**

1. Spring is _____**after**_____ winter.

2. Summer is _____**before**_____ fall.

3. Winter is _____**after**_____ fall.

4. Spring is _____**before**_____ summer.

Steps in a Process

Directions Think about how you brush your teeth.
Draw pictures to show the steps you follow.

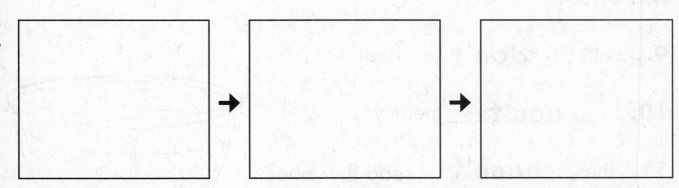

Drawings will vary. Accept all responses that show steps in order.

Copyright © Pearson Education, Inc., or its affiliates. All Rights Reserved.

Contractions With *Not*

Directions Circle the contractions.

1. Please (don't) litter.

2. Cats (can't) fly.

3. I (haven't) finished my homework.

4. My friends (aren't) home.

Directions Write the contractions.

5. can + not **can't**   7. has + not **hasn't**

6. do + not **don't**   8. is + not **isn't**

Directions Finish the sentences. Use the new words you wrote above.

9. Rocks **don't** float.

10. I **can't** hear you.

11. She **hasn't** read that book.

12. That joke **isn't** funny.

Copyright © Pearson Education, Inc., or its affiliates. All Rights Reserved.

Produce Language

My Weekly Concept Journal

Directions   Write your answers in the space provided.

Day 1 <u>**Answers will vary.**</u>

_____

_____

_____

_____

Day 2 _____

_____

_____

_____

Day 3 _____

_____

_____

_____

Day 4 _____

_____

_____

_____

Copyright © Pearson Education, Inc., or its affiliates. All Rights Reserved.

Produce Language

My Weekly Concept Journal

Directions Answer the weekly question.

What do animals do when the seasons change?

Answers will vary but should show
understanding of the Concept Goals:
• understand that the changing of
  seasons affects animals
• explain what it means for an animal to
  migrate
• describe reasons that animals migrate

_____
_____
_____
_____
_____
_____
_____
_____
_____
_____
_____

Copyright © Pearson Education, Inc., or its affiliates. All Rights Reserved.

Surprising Treasures

Vocabulary

grandson	treasure	would
surprise	value	

Directions Match each word to its definition and picture.

1. grandson — the amount of importance that something has

2. surprise — the son of your son or daughter

3. treasure — someone or something with a lot of value

4. value — something that is not expected or usual

Directions Finish the sentences. Use words from the box.

5. His party was a __**surprise**__ .

6. He did not know his grandmother __**would**__ come.

7. She wanted to see her __**grandson**__ .

Copyright © Pearson Education, Inc., or its affiliates. All Rights Reserved.

Name _____

Long a Spelled *ai, ay*

Directions Look at each picture. Say the word. Finish the word.

1. r **ai** n

2. ch **ai** n

3. tr **ai** n

4. cl **ay**

5. tr **ay**

6. p **ay**

Possessives

Directions Read the phrases below. Rewrite using a possessive.

7. the bone that belongs to the dog ___the dog's bone___

8. the feathers that belong to the ducks ___the ducks' feathers___

9. the doll that belongs to the child ___the child's doll___

10. the toys that belong to the kittens ___the kittens' toys___

Copyright © Pearson Education, Inc., or its affiliates. All Rights Reserved.

Interpreting

Directions Look at the pictures. Tell what you think.

1. I think that the dog is ___**hungry**___ .

2. I think that the man is ___**tired**___ .

3. I think that the party is ___**fun**___ .

Draw Conclusions

Directions Look at the pictures. Draw a conclusion about how the person in the picture feels. Begin each sentence with **I think.**

4. I think the girl is happy.

5. I think the boys are sad.

6. I think the man is surprised.

Copyright © Pearson Education, Inc., or its affiliates. All Rights Reserved.

Adjectives

Directions Circle the adjective in each sentence.

1. That man is (tall).

2. He has a (red) ball.

3. I live in a (big) city.

4. The kittens are (little).

5. I like a (soft) pillow.

6. The water is (hot).

Directions Finish each sentence. Use an adjective from the box.

green	cute	tall	red

7. The grass is ____**green**____.

8. I have a ____**red**____ balloon.

9. My dad is very ____**tall**____.

10. My baby brother is ____**cute**____.

Copyright © Pearson Education, Inc., or its affiliates. All Rights Reserved.

Produce Language

My Weekly Concept Journal

Directions Write your answers in the space provided.

Day 1 <u>Answers will vary.</u>
_____
_____
_____
_____

Day 2 _____
_____
_____
_____
_____

Day 3 _____
_____
_____
_____
_____

Day 4 _____
_____
_____
_____
_____

Copyright © Pearson Education, Inc., or its affiliates. All Rights Reserved.

Name _____

Produce Language

My Weekly Concept Journal

Directions Answer the weekly question.

How can a surprise be a treasure?

<u>Answers will vary but should show</u>
<u>understanding of the Concept Goals:</u>
- <u>understand that a surprise can be a</u>
  <u>treasure</u>
- <u>describe a surprise visit from an</u>
  <u>important person</u>

Copyright © Pearson Education, Inc., or its affiliates. All Rights Reserved.

Making Treasures

Vocabulary

card	**create**	**great**
picture	**drew**	

Directions Match each word to its definition and picture.

1. card ——————— a piece of stiff paper with a picture on the front and a message inside

2. picture ——————— a drawing, painting, or photograph

3. create   made lines on paper or some other surface

4. drew   to make something new

Directions Finish the sentences. Use words from the box.

5. She made a __**card or picture**__

6. She _____**drew**_____ a flower.

7. It looked _____**great**_____ .

Copyright © Pearson Education, Inc., or its affiliates. All Rights Reserved.

Name _____

Long e Spelled ea

Directions Look at each picture. Say the word. Finish the word.

1. l **ea** f

2.  t **ea**

3. **ea** st

4. m **ea** t

Inflected Endings (y to i)

Directions Add the endings to the words below. Remember to change the y to i before adding the ending.

5. lucky + er ___**luckier**___

6. cry + ed ___**cried**___

7. try + es ___**tries**___

8. hungry + est ___**hungriest**___

Copyright © Pearson Education, Inc., or its affiliates. All Rights Reserved.

Draw Conclusions

Directions Look at each picture. Finish the sentence.

1. I think that she likes art because

she is drawing .

2. I think that he is happy because

he is laughing .

3. I think that there is a party because
there are balloons and streamers .

Draw Conclusions

Directions Look at each picture. Write a conclusion that you draw from it.

4. I think that **it is a birthday party**
because **I see a birthday cake** .

5. I think that **the dog is dirty**
because **the boy is washing him** .

6. I think that **it is dinner time**

because **the boy is eating** .
Answers will vary. Accept all reasonable answers like those above.

Copyright © Pearson Education, Inc., or its affiliates. All Rights Reserved.

Name _____

Adjectives

Directions Circle the color words.

1. I have a (red) hat.

2. Don't pick the (green) tomatoes.

3. I lost my (blue) mitten.

4. I have a (black) cat.

5. I live in a (white) house.

Directions Finish the sentences. Write a color word on the line.

6. She has a _____ umbrella.

7. The cake has _____ frosting.

8. I used _____ paper to make the card.

9. My dad drives a _____ car.

10. We used _____ paint for my room.

Answers will vary. Accept all reasonable answers that are colors.

Copyright © Pearson Education, Inc., or its affiliates. All Rights Reserved.

Produce Language

My Weekly Concept Journal

Directions Write your answers in the space provided.

Day 1 _Answers will vary._ _____

_____

_____

_____

_____

Day 2 _____

_____

_____

_____

_____

Day 3 _____

_____

_____

_____

_____

Day 4 _____

_____

_____

_____

_____

Copyright © Pearson Education, Inc., or its affiliates. All Rights Reserved.

Name _____

Produce Language

My Weekly Concept Journal

Directions Answer the weekly question.

What treasures can we create?

<u>Answers will vary but should show
understanding of the Concept Goals:</u>
- <u>recognize that people can create</u>
  <u>treasures for other people</u>
- <u>explain how a card we make can be</u>
  <u>a treasure</u>

Copyright © Pearson Education, Inc., or its affiliates. All Rights Reserved.

Our Country's Treasures

Vocabulary

country	found	president
flag	national	took

Directions Match each word to its definition and picture.

1. country   a piece of cloth with a special pattern on it, used as the sign of a country or organization

2. flag   the official leader of a country

3. found   came upon someone or something

4. president   a nation with its land and people

Directions Finish the sentences. Use words from the box.

5. Our ___**country**___ is called the United States.

6. Our ___**national**___ bird is the bald eagle.

7. We ___**took**___ a tour of the White House.

Copyright © Pearson Education, Inc., or its affiliates. All Rights Reserved.

Name _____

Long *o* Spelled *oa, ow*

Directions Look at each picture. Say the word. Finish the word.

1. b **ow** l

2. m **ow**

3. g **oa** l

4. t **oa** d

Three-Letter Blends

Directions Read the words below. Say the words. Circle the letters that blend together.

5. (sc)ratch

6. (sp)latter

7. (st)reet

8. (sp)lash

9. (scr)ub

10. (str)aight

Copyright © Pearson Education, Inc., or its affiliates. All Rights Reserved.

Describing

Directions Complete the sentences that tell about each picture.

1. The Statue of Liberty is _____ **big** _____.

It has ___ **a crown** ___.

2. The Liberty Bell is _____ **large** _____.

It has ___ **a crack** ___.

3. The Capitol is **a white building**.

It has **trees in front of it**.

Answers will vary. Accept all reasonable answers like those above.

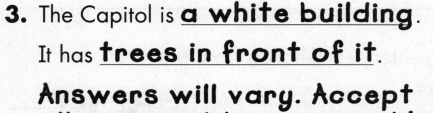

Details and Facts

Directions Tell a fact and two details about the picture.

Fact: The flag is **the symbol of our county**

Detail: It has **red and white stripes**.

Detail: It has **white stars on a blue square**.

Answers will vary. Accept all reasonable answers like those above.

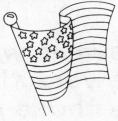

Copyright © Pearson Education, Inc., or its affiliates. All Rights Reserved.

Name _____

Adjectives for Size

Directions Circle the words that tell about size.

(big)	sad	(small)
blue	(short)	(little)
old	happy	sad
(tall)	fast	(long)
red	slow	(thin)

Directions Finish the sentences. Choose from the words you circled above.

1. The White House is _____**big**_____ .

2. The flag pole is _____**tall**_____ .

3. The coin is _____**small**_____ .

4. There is a _____**long**_____ crack on the Liberty Bell.

Answers will vary. Accept all reasonable answers that include adjectives for size like those above.

Copyright © Pearson Education, Inc., or its affiliates. All Rights Reserved.

Produce Language

My Weekly Concept Journal

Directions Write your answers in the space provided.

Day 1 Answers will vary. _____
_____
_____
_____

Day 2 _____
_____
_____
_____

Day 3 _____
_____
_____
_____

Day 4 _____
_____
_____
_____

Copyright © Pearson Education, Inc., or its affiliates. All Rights Reserved.

Name _____

Produce Language

My Weekly Concept Journal

Directions Answer the weekly question.

What treasures can we find in our country?

Answers will vary but should show
understanding of the Concept Goals:
- recognize that the United States has
national treasures
- describe the White House and explain
why the White House is a treasure

Copyright © Pearson Education, Inc., or its affiliates. All Rights Reserved.

Name _____

Special Days

Vocabulary

moon	**above**
fireworks	**celebrate**

Directions Match each word to its definition and picture.

1. moon

explosives that make a lot of bright light and color in the air

2. fireworks

to have a special meal or party because something good has happened

3. above

the large, round object that shines in the sky at night

4. celebrate

in a higher place

Directions Finish the sentences. Use words from the box.

5. We **celebrate** July 4ᵗʰ.

6. There are **fireworks** after dark.

7. There is a full **moon** in the night sky.

Copyright © Pearson Education, Inc., or its affiliates. All Rights Reserved.

Name _____

Long *i* Spelled *ie, igh*

Directions Look at each picture. Say the word. Finish the word.

1. t <u>**ie**</u>

2.  p <u>**ie**</u>

3.  n <u>**igh**</u> t

4. l <u>**igh**</u> t

The Sound /n/ Spelled *kn* and the Sound /r/ Spelled *wr*

Directions Look at each picture. Say the word. Write the word.

5. ____**knob**____

6. ____**knee**____

7. ____**write**____

8. ____**wreath**____

Copyright © Pearson Education, Inc., or its affiliates. All Rights Reserved.

Name _____

Describing

Directions Circle the words that tell *how* people do things.

1. The people in the parade walked (slowly).

2. The band played (loudly).

3. The clowns juggled (happily).

4. The children crossed the street (carefully).

Details and Facts

Directions Write a fact and two details about fireworks.

Fact: **Fireworks are explosives that make bright lights in different colors.**

Detail: **We use fireworks to celebrate the Fourth of July.**

Detail: **Fireworks can be red, yellow, or blue.**

Answers will vary. Accept all reasonable answers like those shown.

Copyright © Pearson Education, Inc., or its affiliates. All Rights Reserved.

Name _____

Adjectives for What Kind

Directions Circle the adjectives.

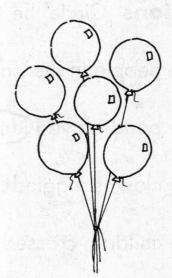

1. The cookies are (sweet)

2. My socks are (blue)

3. This is a (fun) party.

4. We saw (red) and (white) balloons.

Directions Finish the sentences. Write an adjective that tells *what kind* or *what color* on the line.

5. We ate ___**good**___ food.

6. We saw ___**red**___ flags.

7. It was a ___**fun**___ parade.

8. I like ___**noisy**___ celebrations.

9. The fireworks were ___**green**___.

Answers will vary. Accept all reasonable answers like those above.

Copyright © Pearson Education, Inc., or its affiliates. All Rights Reserved.

Produce Language

My Weekly Concept Journal

Directions Write your answers in the space provided.

Day 1 <u>Answers will vary.</u>

_____

_____

_____

_____

Day 2 _____

_____

_____

_____

Day 3 _____

_____

_____

_____

Day 4 _____

_____

_____

_____

_____

Copyright © Pearson Education, Inc., or its affiliates. All Rights Reserved.

Name _____

Produce Language

My Weekly Concept Journal

Directions Answer the weekly question.

Why do we treasure special days?

<u>Answers will vary but should show</u>
<u>understanding of the Concept Goals:</u>
- <u>recognize that we celebrate special</u>
  <u>days</u>
- <u>describe things that people do to</u>
  <u>celebrate special days</u>
- <u>explain why July 4th is a special American</u>
  <u>holiday</u>

Copyright © Pearson Education, Inc., or its affiliates. All Rights Reserved.

Treasures at Home

Vocabulary

family room	**picture**
miss	**brought**

Directions Match each word to its definition and picture.

1. family room   carried or arrived at a new place

2. picture ————— a drawing, painting, or photograph

3. brought   a room in a house where a family spends time together

4. miss ————— to feel sad when someone is not there

Directions Finish the sentences. Use words from the box.

5. Tia and I played in her **family room**.

6. I **brought** my favorite toy.

7. There was a **picture** of her family in the room.

Copyright © Pearson Education, Inc., or its affiliates. All Rights Reserved.

Name _____

Compound Words

Directions Draw a line to separate each compound word into two words.

1. back|pack

2. note|book

3. class|room

4. news|paper

5.  play|ground

---

The Sound /ü/ Spelled *ew, ue, ui*

Directions Look at the picture. Say the word. Write the word.

6. __**juice**__

7. __**clue**__

8.  __**drew**__

Copyright © Pearson Education, Inc., or its affiliates. All Rights Reserved.

Retelling

Directions Circle the words that tell that things happened in the past.

1. I (liked) that picture.

2. We (framed) that photograph.

3. I (missed) my grandparents.

4. I (visited) them last summer.

Character, Setting, Plot

Directions Think of a fairy tale you like. Write about the characters and setting.

5. The characters are _____.

6. The setting is _____.

Answers will vary. Accept all reasonable answers that meet the requirements.

7. Tell about the plot of the story. Draw a picture.

Copyright © Pearson Education, Inc., or its affiliates. All Rights Reserved.

Name _____

Adjectives for How Many

Directions Circle the adjective in each sentence that tells *how many*.

1. There were (many) pictures on the wall.

2. I was in (one) picture.

3. There were a (few) pictures of my mother.

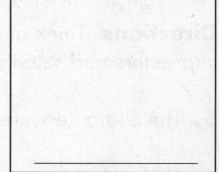

_____

Directions Draw pictures that show one, few, and many things. Write the word **one, few,** or **many** under each picture.

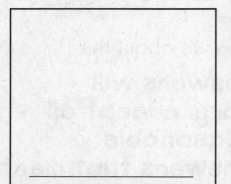

Answers will vary. Accept all pictures that show one, few, and many items.

Copyright © Pearson Education, Inc., or its affiliates. All Rights Reserved.

Produce Language

My Weekly Concept Journal

Directions Write your answers in the space provided.

Day 1 <u>Answers will vary.</u>

_____

_____

_____

Day 2 _____

_____

_____

_____

Day 3 _____

_____

_____

_____

Day 4 _____

_____

_____

_____

Copyright © Pearson Education, Inc., or its affiliates. All Rights Reserved.

Name _____

Produce Language

My Weekly Concept Journal

Directions Answer the weekly question.

What treasures can we share at home?

<u>Answers will vary but should show</u>
<u>understanding of the Concept Goals:</u>
<u>• understand that treasures can be</u>
<u> shared at home</u>
<u>• recognize that a picture of someone</u>
<u> in our family can be a treasure</u>

Copyright © Pearson Education, Inc., or its affiliates. All Rights Reserved.

Our Sharing Treasures

Vocabulary

| because | gate |
| garden | neighbors |

Directions Match each word to its definition and picture.

1. gate — a piece of land where flowers or vegetables are grown

2. neighbors — the part of a wall or fence that you can open like a door

3. garden — people who live near you

Directions Finish the sentences. Use words from the box.

4. I like talking to Sue __**because**__ she is funny.

5. I planted flowers in the __**garden**__.

6. We opened the __**gate**__.

7. We visited our __**neighbors**__.

Copyright © Pearson Education, Inc., or its affiliates. All Rights Reserved.

Name _____

Suffixes *-ly* and *-ful*

Directions Add the suffix *-ly* or *-ful* to each word. Write the new word.

1. quick + ly __**quickly**__

2. sad + ly __**sadly**__

3.  loud + ly __**loudly**__

4. joy + ful __**joyful**__

5.  help + ful __**helpful**__

The Sound /ü/ Spelled *oo*

Directions Look at the picture. Say the word. Write the word.

6. __**moon**__

7. __**spoon**__

8. __**boot**__

Copyright © Pearson Education, Inc., or its affiliates. All Rights Reserved.

Cause-and-Effect Relationship

Directions Look at the picture. Finish each sentence to tell *why* something happened.

1. He mowed the lawn because

the grass was too long .

2. She watered the garden because

it did not rain .

Cause and Effect

Directions Read each sentence. Write the cause and the effect.

3. Marco made a card for his mother because it was her birthday.

The effect is **Marco made a card for his mother**.

The cause is **it was her birthday** .

4. Mom carried the basket because it was too heavy for me.

The effect is **Mom carried the basket** .

The cause is **it was too heavy for me** .

Copyright © Pearson Education, Inc., or its affiliates. All Rights Reserved.

Name _____

Adjectives That Compare

Directions Circle the adjectives that compare.

1. The red tomato is (bigger) than the yellow tomato.

2. The second strawberry was (sweeter) than the first.

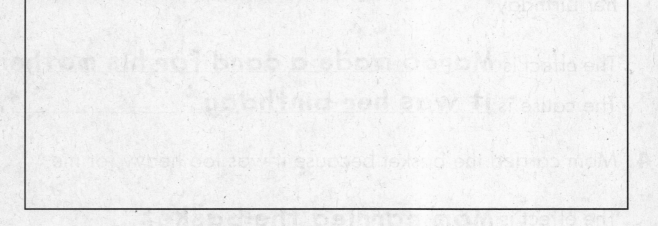

3. Our garden is (smaller) than his.

4. That part of the garden is (wetter) than this part.

5. Some plants grow (taller) than others.

Directions Draw a picture of two trees. One tree is tall. The other tree is taller. Write the adjective that compares under the tree it describes.

<u>**Answers will vary. Accept all reasonable**</u> **answers that meet the requirements.**

Copyright © Pearson Education, Inc., or its affiliates. All Rights Reserved.

Name _____

Produce Language

My Weekly Concept Journal

Directions Write your answers in the space provided.

Day 1 <u>Answers will vary.</u>

_____

_____

_____

Day 2 _____

_____

_____

_____

Day 3 _____

_____

_____

_____

Day 4 _____

_____

_____

_____

Copyright © Pearson Education, Inc., or its affiliates. All Rights Reserved.

Name _____

Produce Language

My Weekly Concept Journal

Directions Answer the weekly question.

What treasures can we share with neighbors?

Answers will vary but should show
understanding of the Concept Goals:
• understand the concept that
   treasures can be shared with neighbors
• describe treasures we can share
   with neighbors, such as vegetables
   from a garden

Copyright © Pearson Education, Inc., or its affiliates. All Rights Reserved.

Solving Problems

Vocabulary

statue	clever	solution	toward
wagon	how	pulled	

Directions Match each word to its definition and picture.

1. statue   a vehicle with four wheels that can be pulled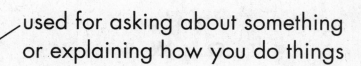

2. wagon   used for asking about something or explaining how you do things

3. how   a shape of a person or animal made of stone, metal, or wood

4. pulled —————— moved something or someone toward yourself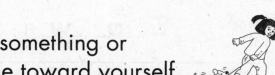

Directions Finish the sentences. Use words from the box.

5. I walked **toward** the school.

6. That was a **clever** idea.

7. I need to find a **solution** to this problem.

Copyright © Pearson Education, Inc., or its affiliates. All Rights Reserved.

Name _____

The Sound /ou/ Spelled *ow*

Directions Look at each picture. Say the word. Finish the word.

1.   __o__ __w__ l

2.   cl __o__ __w__ n

3.   c __o__ __w__

4.   fr __o__ __w__ n

5.   fl __o__ __w__ er

6.   cr __o__ __w__ n

Consonant + *le*

Directions Read the words. Draw a line between the syllables.

7. rid|dle

8. tan|gle

9. bot|tle

10. poo|dle

Copyright © Pearson Education, Inc., or its affiliates. All Rights Reserved.

Comparing and Contrasting

Directions Look at the pictures. Finish the sentences. Tell how the things are different.

1. A grape is ___**sweet**___.

A lemon is ___**sour**___.

2. One horse is ___**big**___.

The other horse is ___**small**___.

3. Ice is ___**cold**___.

Soup is ___**hot**___.

Compare and Contrast

Directions Look at the picture. Tell how the two clowns are alike. Tell how they are different.

4. The clowns are alike.

Both clowns **have dogs, are laughing** _____.

5. The clowns are different.

One clown **has a hat, is wearing a shirt with dots**

The other clown **does not have a hat, is wearing a shirt with a patch**

Answers will vary. Accept all reasonable answers like those above.

Copyright © Pearson Education, Inc., or its affiliates. All Rights Reserved.

Name _____

Commands

Directions Read the sentences. Circle the sentences that are commands.

1. The door is open.

2. (Set the table.)

3. She likes rice.

4. (Brush your teeth.)

5. (Go to bed.)

6. What time is it?

7. She is sleeping.

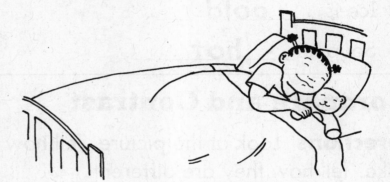

_____

Directions Write a command. Remember to put a period at the end of your sentence.

Answers will vary. Accept all reasonable answers that are a command.

Copyright © Pearson Education, Inc., or its affiliates. All Rights Reserved.

Produce Language

My Weekly Concept Journal

Directions Write your answers in the space provided.

Day 1 <u>Answers will vary.</u> _____

_____

_____

_____

Day 2 _____

_____

_____

_____

Day 3 _____

_____

_____

_____

Day 4 _____

_____

_____

_____

Copyright © Pearson Education, Inc., or its affiliates. All Rights Reserved.

Name _____

Produce Language

My Weekly Concept Journal

Directions Answer the weekly question.

When does a problem need a clever solution?

<u>Answers will vary but should show</u>
<u>understanding of the Concept Goals:</u>
<u>• understand what a problem and</u>
<u>solution are</u>
<u>• identify a problem and a solution</u>
<u>• recognize that some problems may</u>
<u>take a long time to solve</u>

_____

_____

_____

_____

_____

_____

_____

_____

_____

_____

_____

_____

Copyright © Pearson Education, Inc., or its affiliates. All Rights Reserved.

New Ways to Do Things

Vocabulary

airplane	flew	should
clouds	turned	upside down

Directions Match each word to its definition and picture.

1. airplane —————— a vehicle that flies by using wings

2. clouds

moved so that you are looking in a new direction

3. flew ————— moved through the air or wind

4. turned

in a position with the top at the bottom and the bottom on top

5. upside down

white or gray masses in the sky, from which rain falls

Directions Finish the sentences. Use words from the box.

6. I want to fly in a real __**airplane**__ .

7. I want to fly inside __**clouds**__ .

8. You __**should**__ wash your hands before eating.

Copyright © Pearson Education, Inc., or its affiliates. All Rights Reserved.

Name _____

The Sound /ou/ Spelled *ou*

Directions Look at the picture. Say the word. Finish the word.

1. cl__o____u__d

2. m__o____u__se

3. h__o____u__se

4. fl__o____u__r

5. sh__o____u__t

6. c__o____u__ch

VCV Syllables

Directions Read the words. Draw a line between the syllables.

7. pi|lot

9. colo|r

8. riv|er

10. lem|on

Copyright © Pearson Education, Inc., or its affiliates. All Rights Reserved.

Sequencing

Directions Circle the words that show order.

1. (At first), the soup was too hot.

2. (At last), it was just right.

3. (At first), it was raining.

4. (At last), the sun came out.

Sequence

Directions Think about how you brush your teeth. What three things do you need to do in order? Draw pictures to show what you do at first, next, and at last. **Answers will vary.**

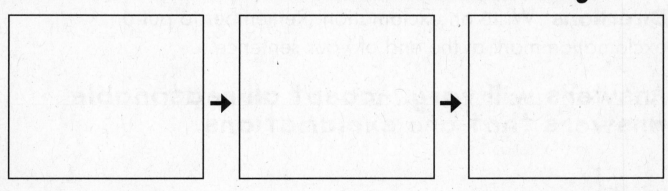

At first, I **put toothpaste on the toothbrush.**

Next, I **brushed my teeth.**

At last, I **rinsed my mouth with water.**

Copyright © Pearson Education, Inc., or its affiliates. All Rights Reserved.

Exclamations

Directions Read the sentences. Circle the ones that are exclamations.

1. She sees an airplane.

2. (Airplanes are loud!)

3. (He did it!)

4. He flew a paper airplane.

5. (The paper airplane flew upside down!)

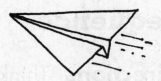

6. (That was amazing!)

Directions Write an exclamation. Remember to put an exclamation mark at the end of your sentence.

Answers will vary. Accept all reasonable answers that are exclamations.

Copyright © Pearson Education, Inc., or its affiliates. All Rights Reserved.

Produce Language

My Weekly Concept Journal

Directions Write your answers in the space provided.

Day 1 <u>Answers will vary.</u> _____

_____

_____

_____

Day 2 _____

_____

_____

_____

Day 3 _____

_____

_____

_____

Day 4 _____

_____

_____

_____

Copyright © Pearson Education, Inc., or its affiliates. All Rights Reserved.

Produce Language

My Weekly Concept Journal

Directions Answer the weekly question.

How can we look at things in a different way?

Answers will vary but should show
underst anding of the Concept Goals:
• understand the concept of solving
   problems by looking at them in
   different ways
• identify different ways to look at
   a problem
• describe how to figure out which
   solution to a problem is best

_____

_____

_____

_____

_____

_____

_____

_____

_____

_____

_____

Copyright © Pearson Education, Inc., or its affiliates. All Rights Reserved.

Solving Mysteries

Vocabulary

| among | closet | looked | solve |
| book | clues | mystery | |

Directions Match each word to its definition and picture.

1. among — a tall cupboard built into the wall of a room, used to store things

2. book — in a group of people or things

3. closet — things that help you find the answer to a difficult problem

4. clues — a set of printed pages held together in a cover so you can read them

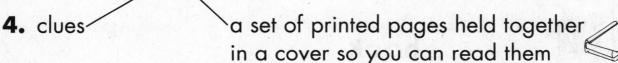

5. looked —————— saw something with your eyes

Directions Finish each sentence. Use words from the box.

6. Where is the ___**book**___ ?

7. Its location is a ___**mystery**___ .

8. I used clues to ___**solve**___ it.

Copyright © Pearson Education, Inc., or its affiliates. All Rights Reserved.

Name _____

The Sound /u/ Spelled *oo*

Directions Look at each picture. Say the word. Write the word.

1. **book**

2. **hood**

3. **foot**

4. **wood**

5. **hook**

Inflected Endings *-s, -es, -ed,* and *-ing*

Directions Add the endings to the words. Write the new word on the line.

6. bat + ed **batted**

7. get + s **gets**

8. slide + es **slides**

9. run + ing **running**

Copyright © Pearson Education, Inc., or its affiliates. All Rights Reserved.

Explaining

Directions Finish the sentences. Tell about something you looked for and found.

1. I looked for my ___**mittens**___.

I found my ___**mittens**___.

2. I looked for my ___**socks**___.

I found my ___**socks**___.

3. I looked for my ___**hat**___.

I found my ___**hat**___.

Main Idea and Details

Directions Read the paragraph. Circle the main idea. Write two details.

⟨Anna wants to find her book.⟩ The book has a red cover. Anna looks in her backpack. There is the book!

Detail: **Possible answer: The book has a red cover.**

Detail: **Possible answer: The book is in Anna's backpack.**

Copyright © Pearson Education, Inc., or its affiliates. All Rights Reserved.

Name _____

How Sentences Begin and End

Directions Fix what is wrong with each sentence. Write the sentence correctly on the line.

1. where is my coat ___**Where is my coat?**___

2. it is not in the closet **It is not in the closet.**

3. here it is _____**Here it is!**_____

Directions Write a sentence about each picture. Remember to begin with a capital letter and use an ending mark.

4. __Possible answer: The mother__ __is reading a book to her child.__

5. __Possible answer: The__ __detective is looking for clues.__

Copyright © Pearson Education, Inc., or its affiliates. All Rights Reserved.

Produce Language

My Weekly Concept Journal

Directions Write your answers in the space provided.

Day 1 <u>Answers will vary.</u>

_____

_____

_____

Day 2 _____

_____

_____

_____

Day 3 _____

_____

_____

_____

Day 4 _____

_____

_____

_____

Copyright © Pearson Education, Inc., or its affiliates. All Rights Reserved.

Name _____

Produce Language

My Weekly Concept Journal

Directions Answer the weekly question.

How do we solve mysteries?

<u>Answers will vary but should show</u>
<u>understanding of the Concept Goals:</u>
- <u>understand that a mystery is a problem</u>
  <u>we need to solve</u>
- <u>recognize that clues can help us solve</u>
  <u>mysteries</u>

_____

_____

_____

_____

_____

_____

_____

_____

_____

_____

_____

_____

Copyright © Pearson Education, Inc., or its affiliates. All Rights Reserved.

Ideas That Make Life Easier

Vocabulary

bikes	enjoy	idea	today
horses	gas	oil	

Directions Match each word to its definition and picture.

1. bikes   thick, dark liquid that makes machines work smoothly

2. horses   a thought or plan that you think of

3. gas   large animals that people ride on and use for pulling heavy things

4. idea   more than one bicycle

5. oil   a liquid that makes cars and trucks move

Directions Finish the sentences. Use words from the box.

6. I ____**enjoy**____ riding my bike.

7. We rode our bikes ____**today**____.

8. We saw ____**horses**____ in a field.

Copyright © Pearson Education, Inc., or its affiliates. All Rights Reserved.

Name _____

The Sound /oi/ Spelled *oi, oy*

Directions Look at each picture. Say the word. Write the word.

1.   <u>**boy**</u>

2.   <u>**toy**</u>

3.   <u>**coin**</u>

4.    <u>**boil**</u>

Suffixes *-er* and *-or*

Directions Look at each picture. Say the word. Write the word.

5.    <u>**teacher**</u>

6.    <u>**inventor**</u>

7.   <u>**runner**</u>

Copyright © Pearson Education, Inc., or its affiliates. All Rights Reserved.

Describing

Directions Circle the words that tell *where*.

1. The shoe is (under) the bed.

2. The newspaper is (behind) the chair.

3. The light is (above) the table.

4. He is hiding (behind) the couch.

5. The cat is (under) the table.

6. The shelf is (above) the desk.

Graphic Sources

Directions Finish the sentences. Use the graphic source to help you.

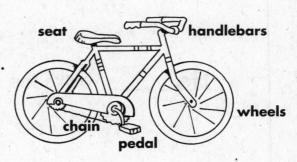

seat handlebars chain pedal wheels

7. The seat is _____**behind**_____ the handlebars.

8. The handlebars are _____**above**_____ the chain.

9. The chain is _____**under**_____ the seat.

Copyright © Pearson Education, Inc., or its affiliates. All Rights Reserved.

Pronouns

Directions Circle the pronouns.

1. (He) rides a horse.

2. (She) rides a bike.

3. (It) is a car.

4. (You) have a great idea.

5. (We) enjoy all kinds of games.

6. (They) have a new car.

Directions Finish the sentences. Use a pronoun.

7. _____**He**_____ walks the dog.

8. _____**They**_____ play soccer.

9. _____**She**_____ enjoys her book.

Copyright © Pearson Education, Inc., or its affiliates. All Rights Reserved.

Produce Language

My Weekly Concept Journal

Directions Write your answers in the space provided.

Day 1 <u>Answers will vary.</u>

_____

_____

_____

Day 2 _____

_____

_____

_____

Day 3 _____

_____

_____

_____

_____

Day 4 _____

_____

_____

_____

Copyright © Pearson Education, Inc., or its affiliates. All Rights Reserved.

Name _____

Produce Language

My Weekly Concept Journal

Directions Answer the weekly question.

How can a great idea make our lives easier?

Answers will vary but should show
understanding of the Concept Goals:
- recognize that ideas can change our
  world
- identify and describe inventions that
  have made our lives easier
- describe how cars have made our lives
  easier

_____

_____

_____

_____

_____

_____

_____

_____

_____

_____

_____

_____

Copyright © Pearson Education, Inc., or its affiliates. All Rights Reserved.

Name _____

Ideas That Change Lives

Vocabulary

| because | phones | mail |
| letters | changed | learn |

Directions Match each word to its definition and picture.

1. letters

to get knowledge of something or the ability to do something

2. phones

written messages that you put into an envelope and send to someone by mail

3. mail

the letters and packages that are delivered to a place

4. learn

objects that you use to speak to someone in another place

Directions Finish the sentences. Use words from the box.

5. Phones __**changed**__ the way people talk.

6. __**Because**__ of phones, it is easier to talk to people who live far away.

7. I still like to get __**mail**__ though.

Copyright © Pearson Education, Inc., or its affiliates. All Rights Reserved.

Name _____

The Sound /ȯ/ Spelled aw, au

Directions Look at each picture. Say the word. Write the word.

1. _____ **saw** _____

2.  _____ **paw** _____

3. _____ **yawn** _____

4.  _____ **author** _____

The Sound /e/ Spelled ea

Directions Look at each picture. Say the word. Write the word.

5. _____ **ahead** _____

6. _____ **head** _____

7. _____ **bread** _____

Copyright © Pearson Education, Inc., or its affiliates. All Rights Reserved.

Asking Questions

Directions Write a question about each picture.

1. What <u>**is he reading**</u> ?

2. Who <u>**is on the phone**</u> ?

3. What <u>**is in the bowl**</u> ?

Answers will vary. Accept all reasonable answers like those above.

Draw Conclusions

Directions Write a conclusion about each picture.

4. <u>**The dog was dirty.**</u>

5. <u>**They are having fun.**</u>
   <u>**It is cold.**</u>

6. <u>**It is the girl's**</u>
   <u>**birthday.**</u>

Answers will vary. Accept all reasonable answers like those above.

Copyright © Pearson Education, Inc., or its affiliates. All Rights Reserved.

Name _____

Pronouns *I* and *Me*

Directions Circle **I** and **me** in the sentences.

1. Someone called (me) on the phone.

2. (I) like to talk on the phone.

3. (I) answer the phone when it rings.

4. Sometimes the call is not for (me).

5. (I) tell my parents who is on the phone.

Directions Finish the sentences. Use the pronouns **I** and **me.**

6. __I__ wrote a letter to my grandmother.

7. __I__ put the letter in the mailbox.

8. She called **me** on my birthday.

Directions Write a sentence about something you like to do. Use the pronoun **I.**

9. __Answers will vary but should begin with the pronoun I.__

Copyright © Pearson Education, Inc., or its affiliates. All Rights Reserved.

Produce Language

My Weekly Concept Journal

Directions Write your answers in the space provided.

Day 1 <u>Answers will vary.</u> _____

_____

_____

_____

Day 2 _____

_____

_____

_____

Day 3 _____

_____

_____

_____

Day 4 _____

_____

_____

_____

Copyright © Pearson Education, Inc., or its affiliates. All Rights Reserved.

Name _____

Produce Language

My Weekly Concept Journal

Directions Answer the weekly question.

How can a great idea change the way we live?

<u>Answers will vary but should show</u>
<u>understanding of the Concept Goals:</u>
- <u>understand that a great idea can</u>
  <u>change the way we live</u>
- <u>recognize that a great idea can be</u>
  <u>helpful, fun, or both</u>
- <u>explain how phones have changed</u>
  <u>people's lives</u>

_____

_____

_____

_____

_____

_____

_____

_____

_____

_____

_____

Copyright © Pearson Education, Inc., or its affiliates. All Rights Reserved.

New Ideas

Vocabulary

robot	build	loose	untie
shoelaces	different	retie	

Directions Match each word to its definition and picture.

1. robot —————— a machine that moves and works instead of a person

2. shoelaces ⟋ to fasten things with a rope or string again

3. build —————— to make something by putting pieces together

4. retie ⟋ long pieces of string that are used to make shoes fit tightly on your feet

5. untie —————— to take apart a knot or something that is tied

Directions Finish the sentences. Use words from the box.

6. Wendy had a __**different**__ idea.

7. She wanted to fix the robot's __**loose**__ arm.

Copyright © Pearson Education, Inc., or its affiliates. All Rights Reserved.

Name _____

Prefixes *un-* and *re-*

Directions Add the prefix *un-* or *re-* to the following words.
Write the new words.

1. un + tie _____**untie**_____

2. un + lock _____**unlock**_____

3.  re + write _____**rewrite**_____

4. re + paint _____**repaint**_____

Long *o* Spelled *o*

Directions Look at the picture. Say the word. Write the word.

5. _____**robot**_____

6.  _____**gold**_____

7. _____**ocean**_____

Copyright © Pearson Education, Inc., or its affiliates. All Rights Reserved.

Comparing

Directions Circle the *-er* words below.

1. An airplane can go (faster) than a car.

2. A robot can work (longer) than a person.

3. My father's shoes are (bigger) than mine.

4. The ocean is (deeper) than the lake.

5. The clouds are (higher) than the house.

Comparing and Contrasting

Directions Look at the picture. Tell how the kites are alike. Tell one way they are different.

6. Compare They are both _____**kites**_____.

7. Contrast One is **a rectangle**, and the other is **a diamond**.

Answers will vary. Accept all reasonable answers like those above.

Copyright © Pearson Education, Inc., or its affiliates. All Rights Reserved.

Name _____

More About Pronouns

Directions Circle the pronouns.

1. Anna showed her robot to (us).

2. Luis played with (it).

3. The robot walked behind (you).

4. The robot stopped next to (him).

5. Luis gave the robot back to (her).

_____

Directions Finish the sentences. Use pronouns.

6. Maria walked with _____.

7. Eric played that game with _____.

8. Mom baked a cake for _____.

9. Fred liked _____.

10. The shoes do not fit _____.

Answers will vary. Accept all reasonable answers that are pronouns.

Copyright © Pearson Education, Inc., or its affiliates. All Rights Reserved.

Produce Language

My Weekly Concept Journal

Directions Write your answers in the space provided.

Day 1 Answers will vary.
_____
_____
_____
_____

Day 2 _____
_____
_____
_____
_____

Day 3 _____
_____
_____
_____
_____

Day 4 _____
_____
_____
_____
_____

Copyright © Pearson Education, Inc., or its affiliates. All Rights Reserved.

Name _____

Produce Language

My Weekly Concept Journal

Directions Answer the weekly question.

What can happen when someone has a new idea?

Answers will vary but should show
understanding of the Concept Goals:
- understand that new ideas can result in
something that other people can use
- describe what can happen when someone
has a new idea

Copyright © Pearson Education, Inc., or its affiliates. All Rights Reserved.